Warrior Renew

Lori S. Katz, PhD, is a clinical psychologist who has worked for the Department of Veterans Affairs for over 20 years specializing in the treatment of military sexual trauma. She was the founder/director of a women's mental health center and developed a sexual trauma treatment program that included supportive housing for homeless women veterans. She has been recognized as a "subject matter expert" and as such she worked on a Department of Defense task force to develop new policies for the care of victims of sexual assault. Her work has been the topic of local, national, and international news reports. She is a researcher, clinician, and public speaker on the topic of military sexual trauma.

Warrior Renew: Healing From Military Sexual Trauma

Lori S. Katz, PhD

SPRINGER PUBLISHING COMPANY
NEW YORK

Springer Publishing Company, LLC
11 West 42nd Street
New York, NY 10036
www.springerpub.com

Acquisitions Editor: Nancy S. Hale
Production Editor: Shelby Peak
Composition: diacriTech
Original artwork: Lori S. Katz

ISBN: 978-0-8261-2231-5
e-book ISBN: 978-0-8261-2232-2

14 15 16 17 / 5 4 3 2 1

The author and the publisher of this Work have made every effort to use sources believed to be reliable to provide information that is accurate and compatible with the standards generally accepted at the time of publication. The author and publisher shall not be liable for any special, consequential, or exemplary damages resulting, in whole or in part, from the readers' use of, or reliance on, the information contained in this book. The publisher has no responsibility for the persistence or accuracy of URLs for external or third-party Internet websites referred to in this publication and does not guarantee that any content on such websites is, or will remain, accurate or appropriate.

Library of Congress Cataloging-in-Publication Data
Katz, Lori S., 1963-
  Warrior renew : healing from military sexual trauma / Lori S. Katz, PhD.
    pages cm
  Includes bibliographical references and index.
  ISBN 978-0-8261-2231-5 — ISBN 978-0-8261-2232-2 (e-book)
  1. Sexual abuse victims—Rehabilitation. 2. Psychic trauma—Treatment. 3. Sexual harassment in the military. 4. Women soldiers—Mental health. 5. Women soldiers—Crime against. 6. Self-help techniques. I. Title.
  RC560.S44K38 2014
  616.85'8369008697—dc23
                                                                                                    2014020373

A Facilitator's Guide for *Warrior Renew* is available for group leaders and facilitators. Please visit www.WarriorRenew.com for more information.

Printed in the United States of America by Bradford & Bigelow.

This workbook is dedicated to all of the courageous men and women who have incurred the wounds of sexual trauma while serving in the U.S. military: Army, Navy, Marines, Air Force, Coast Guard, National Guard, and Reserves. It is an honor to serve you.

Contents

Foreword

It is a privilege to write the Foreword for this first-ever workbook to assist men and women who have been victimized by military sexual trauma (MST). To give a brief history, I met Dr. Lori S. Katz in 1993 during my employment at the Department of Veterans Affairs (VA), West Los Angeles, California. The VA Long Beach and the VA West Los Angeles women veterans programs worked together to establish a "one-stop shop" for our women veterans combining primary care, gynecology, and mental health in one women's health clinic. These sites had two of the first funded full-time Women Veteran Program Managers, myself and Diane Guilano, RN (Long Beach), which allowed us the flexibility to coordinate our efforts. Dr. Katz was instrumental in guiding us through some very difficult treatment plans for our patients identified as having MST. Several of the women verbalized their feeling of safety once they entered treatment with Dr. Katz. She also provided us with educational classes that allowed us to more effectively treat our MST patients.

Knowing the results of Dr. Katz's work and the many lives that she has changed, I am delighted to endorse Dr. Katz's *Warrior Renew* workbook for men and women seeking healing from MST. Although the high prevalence rates of MST are discouraging, I am confident that *Warrior Renew* can reach many, many MST survivors and provide the hope and healing that they need, for all of those across the country and throughout the military.

Lt. Col. Patricia Jackson-Kelley
Veteran of the U.S. Air Force and Air Force, Army, and Navy Reserves,
Los Angeles County Military and Veterans Affairs Commissioner
Former Women Veteran Program Manager,
Department of Veterans Affairs, Greater Los Angeles Healthcare System

Preface

Warrior Renew is based on a treatment approach that the author has been developing for many years while treating those with military sexual trauma (MST). It is a combination of the best lessons and most effective exercises—refined, revised, and tested—and then packaged into a systematic and comprehensive approach for healing MST. This manual can also be used for those who have experienced childhood and/or adult sexual trauma and abuse. It is not limited for use with any particular diagnosis such as posttraumatic stress disorder or depression, but rather addresses common symptoms and reactions to sexual trauma across diagnoses.

There are several values underlying the *Warrior Renew* program. First of all, it is assumed that everyone "makes sense." There is a good reason why people respond to trauma the way they do. This insight and connection to understanding the past can be a great relief in itself, but can also assist in releasing old patterns and building new, more positive ones. Second, healing is a process of resolving the past by rethinking or reprocessing it in the present—it is a process achieved by toggling among thinking, feeling, and moving. *Warrior Renew* is intended to be an interactive program designed to help readers by offering education on MST-related topics and opportunities for self-discovery in a context of support, caring, and validation. Third, healing is about releasing the emotional constriction that inevitably surrounds trauma. This means not only moving through painful material, but also reconnecting with positive factors such as optimism and self-esteem, and being able to connect with others and experience joy. Many participants find the program to be validating, engaging, and, as it is intended, *fun*! Although this may seem counterintuitive, it is equally important to learn to laugh as it is to learn to cry—and sometimes having fun is a great way to motivate learning, teach tolerance of negative emotions, build trust and community, and facilitate releasing old pains.

Ultimately, the intention of Warrior Renew *is to help readers become free from the burdens of the past so they may welcome a productive and affirming future.*

> *Note:* This book is meant to be gender neutral, designed for both men and women. Thus, pronouns of both genders will be used throughout the workbook. Also, the words "victim" and "survivor" will be used in this text to refer to those who have been attacked or have endured events of sexual trauma and to those who have carried on, persevered, recovered, and/or are seeking recovery. Readers of this text are most likely both.

Acknowledgments

First of all, thank you to Seymour Epstein, a brilliant and proficient psychologist whose work on cognitive-experiential self-theory has been a guiding foundation for my work. Dr. Epstein is also a valued mentor and role model who has my utmost respect.

Next, thank you to Jane Hammerslough, LMFT, for her support and contributions to this book. Ms. Hammerslough is an accomplished writer, having authored over 30 books for adults and young readers, and is a frequent contributor to magazines and newspapers. She is also the winner of the Award for Excellence from Parenting Publications of America. Ms. Hammerslough is a cherished colleague and her input is much appreciated.

Thank you to Lt. Col. Kelley for her kind and encouraging words. Lt. Col. Kelley has had an impressive career in the military and serving veterans. It is an honor to know her.

Finally, thank you to Nancy S. Hale and Springer Publishing Company, who share the passion for addressing military sexual trauma and realize the importance of this topic by supporting the publication of this book.

Orientation

■ Opening exercises: Group introductions (see Appendix A)

Note: All weeks after Orientation begin with an opening exercise and end with a closing exercise as described in Appendix A and Appendix B.

OVERVIEW OF *WARRIOR RENEW*

The *Warrior Renew* program was designed to address unique aspects of military sexual trauma (MST). It gives participants (1) skills to manage trauma symptoms, (2) tools to address unresolved issues such as injustice and self-blame, (3) guidance toward radical acceptance of the past, and (4) the inspiration to move forward in one's life in a meaningful way. In addition, it delves into interpersonal issues, where MST may have disrupted the ability to form secure relationships with others. By definition, MST is an interpersonal type of trauma (it happened with another person), often characterized by betrayal, shame, and lack of support from others—leading to resentments, unrealistic self-blame, difficulties with sexuality, and avoidance of emotional and physical intimacy.

This workbook provides a variety of ways to understand, process, and ultimately overcome sexual trauma and abuse and its effects. It is divided into 12 chapters. The first chapter discusses "What is military sexual trauma?" This chapter explores this trauma and the many physical, mental, emotional, and social repercussions it may have on the lives of those who have experienced it. In the next chapter, feelings are discussed as helpful and adaptive responses from our thoughts where "feelings give us valuable information." In Chapter 3, readers learn how to cope with nightmares and ways to develop good sleep habits to promote sound sleep. Chapter 4 discusses "triggers" or sudden feelings of anxiety or panic that are associated with trauma. In addition, skills are offered to help readers tolerate and release intense feelings. In Chapters 5 and 6, readers learn ways to deal with important feelings such as anger, resentment, guilt, self-blame, and shame. The focus in Chapters 7 and 8 is on memories of trauma, holograms, and defining relationship patterns. In Chapter 9, readers learn important skills for recognizing and dealing with feelings of loss and grief. Chapter 10 discusses a developmental model for romantic relationships, how to rekindle trust, and healthy sexuality, and it explores what each reader feels is an ideal relationship. In Chapter 11, readers learn skills for improving communication. Finally, Chapter 12 assists readers in developing ways for finding meaning, empowerment, and joy after experiencing trauma and beyond. Throughout each chapter, exercises guide, encourage, and help readers to explore their own feelings and thoughts about their experiences.

COGNITIVE-EXPERIENTIAL SELF-THEORY

Seymour Epstein is a well-known psychologist whose work on cognitive-experiential self-theory (CEST; Epstein, 1990, 1991, 2014) is a guiding theoretical foundation for *Warrior Renew*. In this model, Epstein demonstrates that we have two basic ways of processing information, the *cognitive-rational* system and the *experiential* system. The *cognitive-rational* system processes information in an intellectual way, while the *experiential* system processes information in an emotional way. Trauma is an emotional experience and, therefore, by activating the experiential system, information can be accessed about the trauma. Similarly, Epstein proposes that in order to affect deep and lasting change, that change needs to occur in the experiential system. This can be achieved through either new lived experiences or imaginal experiences (imagery). (More about this will be presented in the text.) Thus, *Warrior Renew* activates the experiential system in several ways: (1) opening exercises (interactive games) help participants feel better, increase safety, build a sense of community, and assist participants in feeling more present and "in their bodies" before learning the text; (2) class time itself is designed to be a healing experience including insights, discussions, imagery, and journaling; and (3) closing exercises (relaxation activities) allow participants to experience the neuro-emotional effects of "quieting the mind."

A HOLOGRAPHIC REPROCESSING APPROACH FOR HEALING TRAUMA

Based on the theories of Epstein's CEST, Lori S. Katz developed a psychotherapy model called Holographic Reprocessing (HR; see Basharpoor, Narimani, Gamari-give, Abolgasemi, & Molavi, 2011; Katz, 2001, 2005; Katz et al., 2008; Katz et al., 2014). A brief explanation is that HR works holistically—with the "whole person"—addressing recurrent patterns that can occur in people's lives and relationships. The treatment includes identifying patterns consisting of thoughts, feelings, and behaviors, but it is people's experience (both past and present) that ultimately either reinforces (strengthens) or changes the pattern of thoughts, feelings, and behaviors. Positive new experiences weaken old patterns and set the stage to create new, more healthy ones.

In this model, participants are not required to relive or recount specific events of trauma. In fact, *there is no sharing of trauma stories during group*. Participants will not be required to write about specific events of trauma, but may do so if they feel it would be helpful. In the HR model, it is acknowledged that these events have already occurred. Instead of recalling what has happened, the focus is on how trauma has affected people's lives. HR examines the total impact of having lived through trauma and all of its consequences. In other words, instead of focusing on a specific event of trauma, the focus is on the person who has experienced trauma and the resulting relational patterns, including perceptions about oneself, others, and the world. These perceptions are the focus of treatment. By taking an objective viewpoint, participants can think in new ways about themselves and others—considering context and other people's motives and agendas. HR also helps people heal through self-compassion, encouragement, and awakening possibilities for a better future.

A TRANSFORMATIONAL APPROACH TO HEALING

There are many ways to help people who have experienced sexual trauma and abuse, all of which have their own merit and value. Some approaches seek to reduce symptoms such as lessening the severity of depression, improving sleep, or reducing avoidance or panic attacks. This is very helpful when people are suffering from such intense symptoms that they have difficulty functioning. However, in addition to providing coping skills and education, this book also aspires to help people address that which causes the symptoms, rather than simply to manage or reduce the symptoms. In other words, participants in this program learn to consider the core or root of the issues that cause pain and how to see it in an entirely new way. Thus, the term "transformational" is used because participants have permanent change when they heal that which remains unresolved, haunting, or unsettling deep inside of them.

A GUIDE FOR USING THIS TEXT

Note: A separate facilitator's handbook (Katz, 2014) discusses program design (e.g., outpatient, residential, and accelerated), guidance for facilitators, and outcome research.

If you are using this manual in a group, then establishing certain agreements and rules will help the group run smoothly. The following section is a description of what group members can expect. It covers the basic structure and format, confidentiality, and the starting and ending processes. This way everyone is informed and can start with the same expectations.

Using This Text in a Group

Groups seem to run best when kept small (no fewer than 4 and no larger than 15), with the optimum number between 8 and 12 group members. Groups also seem to run best if everyone is committed to attending all sessions, participating in the discussions, and doing the suggested opening and closing exercises. There will always be differences in a group. These differences can add to the richness of the discussion by highlighting new points of view. However, if the differences are too great, they could be disruptive to the flow of the group. It is recommended that a group have a strong leader/facilitator who can keep the group on task, facilitate discussion, handle upsets and disagreements, and balance the level of work with humor and fun (for details, please see facilitator's handbook, Katz, 2014).

The leader can also prescreen group participants to make sure everyone is a good match with each other as well as determine if they are safe, ready, and able to participate in group. For example, if someone has been feeling suicidal within the past 90 days, has less than 90 days of sobriety, has multiple medical or legal appointments interfering with attendance, is in the process of changing medications, or is taking medications that cause drowsiness to the extent that it could impair one's ability to participate, then it may not be the right time for that person to participate in this group. It is up to the group facilitator to determine admission to the group with the intention of supporting participants so they can be successful and benefit from the program.

Setting Expectations

It is important for group members to know what is expected of them and what they can expect from the group. This is also called *informed consent*. Informed consent covers content, group rules, confidentiality, and the time and place of meeting. The group should decide on their agreed-upon policies for food, being late, cancellations, breaking privacy, and providing peer support between group sessions.

It is suggested that participants follow these four expectations:

1. **Show up** (even when you don't feel like it)
2. **Focus on your own healing** (do not try to help others and avoid helping yourself)
3. **Respect yourself** (take care of yourself; shower, eat well, drink water, and rest)
4. **Respect others** (listen when they talk; speak with kindness and patience; and respect other people's boundaries, confidentiality/ privacy, and personal space)

Starting and Ending on Time

Starting and ending the group on time sets an expectation that everyone is serious about the group. James Lang, MD, discussed beginning and ending times as part of the "brass tacks" of psychotherapy. This term was derived from building furniture, where the brass tacks kept upholstery in place on top of a frame. Brass tacks in therapy keep the therapy in place—keeping the group intact and cohesive and providing containment, boundaries, and safety for the group. Besides starting and ending on time, brass tacks also include meeting at a consistent place and at the same time and day of the week. It is important to maintain a structure for the group so participants will want to continue to attend. Changes in these brass tacks usually lead to dropouts, no-shows, confusion, and forgotten appointments.

If one person is missing, still start the group on time. If someone comes in late, politely invite him or her to join the group but continue the group (although you can briefly summarize what has already transpired if it flows with the group). If one person is chronically late, then this can be disruptive to the rest of the group. This may come up in a group discussion or the leader may want to have a private discussion with that individual to find out what he or she may need in order to get to the group on time.

Confidentiality

There are certain laws regarding confidentiality for licensed professionals. That means professionals cannot disclose anything about group participants. If this applies to your group leaders, they will discuss the limits of confidentiality that they must uphold, such as if they are mandated reporters of child or elder abuse. They may also discuss how they will handle participants who threaten to harm themselves or others, and if group participation will be documented in a medical record. All of these issues regarding confidentiality should be discussed with the group to make sure that everyone is informed and agrees to participate in the group knowing the rules.

Although there is no confidentiality among group members, there is an assumed level of trust and privacy among all participants in a group. In order for people to feel safe to share their feelings, the group needs to be a safe place both in group and outside of group. This means having a shared agreement that nobody will discuss what is shared in group outside of group. Of course this cannot be enforced and there are no laws governing group confidentiality, but for the sake of the group, participants are asked to honor the privacy of others. If friendships are formed, it is especially important to continue to honor the rule of not discussing other group members outside of group. In addition, participants are asked not to discuss their past traumas, suicidal behaviors, or other personal details related to trauma with other group members. This can be shared with an individual therapist.

Can you think of why it would not be a good idea to share this information with other group members?

Eating/Drinking During Group

It is common in our society to equate gathering a group of people with offering food and drinks. However, when running a group food can be a distraction, disruption, and avoidance strategy to not deal with emotional topics. Since this is a course on dealing with trauma, it would be counterproductive to provide such a distraction. A group member can also be perceived as disengaged or even rude if he or she is eating when someone else is sharing. Besides, food can be messy (e.g., spilling on workbooks) and loud (e.g., crunching and slurping). Therefore, it is suggested to leave food out of group. If everyone wants to have food this should be limited to either before or after the group.

Drinks can also be used as an avoidance strategy, especially if the drink contains caffeine or other stimulant (e.g., power drinks). However, people do get thirsty. It is recommended that drinking water be allowed in groups. Again, refreshments such as coffee/tea and cookies/fruit can be served before or after group if that is what everyone wants, but it is recommended that participants focus on group during group time. (This also includes no chewing gum, eating candy, sucking on lollipops, cracking sunflower seeds, and so on!)

Storing Books Between Sessions

Although the group may have mixed feelings about this issue, it is suggested that all books are stored in a locked cabinet between sessions in a secure location (such as in a therapist's office). This way, the books are ready and available for each group and nobody forgets or loses his or her book, spills coffee on it, or has the dog chew it up! At the end of the course, participants can keep their books. However, if participants want to keep their books, then they are responsible for bringing the books to class and keeping their books safe between classes.

Opening and Closing Group Sessions

It is suggested that groups begin with a few exercises to help participants feel present, grounded in their bodies, and connected to the group. This will also help participants retain and process information during the group. Although unconventional for a class, these opening exercises help participants explore themes such as safety, trust, power, balance, self-expression, sound, imagination, play, and laughter using nonverbal holistic approaches. In the process, these experiences strengthen the bonds among group members and facilitate a deepening of the group process. One former participant said she had not laughed so much since before the trauma. Another participant said that at first she thought the exercises were kind of silly and uncomfortable, but by the end she felt they really helped her access her feelings and become more comfortable with herself (within her own body) and with other people.

For example, at the beginning of group everyone can stand in a circle. The facilitator leads the exercise of slowly raising her arms with an inhalation, holding the breath at the top for 5 seconds, and then slowly exhaling and releasing her arms. Participants are instructed to feel the connection between the breath and the movements of the arms. They are also instructed to extend the arms all the way through the fingertips, feeling the energy through the arms and hands. This breathing sequence is repeated three times.

The group can also engage in a quick "new game" or an interactive exercise. One such exercise is to instruct everyone to move around the room in a random fashion, filling all the spaces in the room. They are told that they are a giant water molecule moving about. Then the instructor says the water molecule is put in the freezer and everyone begins to move in slow motion—still moving, but slower and slower until they are practically frozen. Then the water molecule comes back to room temperature. Next the water molecule is put on the stove and begins to heat up. Accordingly participants begin to move faster around the room. Then the water molecule comes back to room temperature. At the end of the exercise participants clap for their efforts. A list of interactive games is included in Appendix A of this text.

Closure is also important for the group. At the end of the session, it is suggested that the group take a few minutes to do a relaxation exercise. This could be guided imagery, quietly listening to soothing music, chanting a sound, or simply sitting quietly. Afterward, end with two to three *cleansing breaths* (deep breaths through the nose and out of the mouth with a sigh). A list of closing exercises are included in Appendix B of this text.

Group Format

It is suggested that two sessions are devoted to each chapter. The first two classes are for orientation, covering participant introductions, reviewing group rules and confidentiality, and discussing what to expect. All subsequent chapters would also have two class sessions devoted to them, allowing time for some flexibility, writing assignments, and discussion. The last two sessions would include a class for review of the material and the final class for graduation (see Appendix C). The following format is suggested for an outpatient group that meets twice a week. See Katz (2014) for other program designs.

Suggested Format for a 2-Hour Group That Meets Twice a Week			
Session 1		**Session 2**	
Opening exercise	(15 minutes)	Opening exercise	(15 minutes)
Class	(90 minutes)	Class	(90 minutes)
Closing exercise	(15 minutes)	Closing exercise	(15 minutes)

Benefits of Covering a Single Chapter Over Two Sessions

Although the content of the chapters can be quickly read within one session, fully absorbing the information and participating in the exercises and discussion requires time. Some concepts may be easy to understand intellectually but require some work to fully understand or "get it" emotionally. Thus, it is suggested that groups not rush through the material but rather use the time as part of the healing process. A concept that is discussed on Day 1 may at first be confusing, but, after thinking about it outside of group, participants may find that it makes better sense by the second session of the chapter. Participants may want a quick review before proceeding with the second session.

After the opening exercises, the suggested format of a session is for the participants to take turns reading a paragraph or two, continuing around the circle. The facilitator can stop the reading for discussion, ask and answer questions, or allow time to complete exercises. The facilitator maintains the timing, flow, and group discussion, and establishes a good stopping point midway through the chapter.

Did You Know . . .

It is normal to have mixed feelings about starting a program like *Warrior Renew.* It may be both exciting and terrifying, and you may be filled with many hopes as well as fears. It is typical to have concerns when you embark on a new adventure. And *Warrior Renew* is a new adventure, an adventure into yourself. But you are not alone: You have an expert guidebook that has taken hundreds of MST survivors on this road before, you have a skilled facilitator to lead you, and you have a community of fellow travelers going through this adventure with you. Right now when you look out on the road ahead, it may seem long and difficult, and maybe the bags you are carrying are just a little too heavy. All we ask is that you show up and participate. There may be times when you want to sit on the side of the road or even give up. And still all we ask is that you show up and participate. Then without even being aware of it, all of a sudden you might notice that your bag got a little lighter. You might notice that you are stronger, have more energy, and can make it with a lot less effort than you thought. This is the beauty of transformation. So just show up and participate even when you are tired or don't feel like it. Maybe one particular class is the class that gives you a special insight or breakthrough. Maybe the person you find most annoying in the class is the one who helps you see a hidden part of yourself. Welcome the challenges! You might be surprised at what happens for you!

GROUP AGREEMENTS

Please read these agreements out loud with the group and discuss any points of concern. If everyone agrees, sign that you agree to abide by the rules.

Agreements for the Participants of the Group

1. I agree to show up on time, stay for the entire class, and turn off my cell phone.

2. I agree that all personal information shared in the group stays in the group. If I am friends with a group member outside of the group, I agree to not discuss information about other people. I agree to respect the privacy of others.

3. If I ask another participant for help, then I must be willing to accept help from that person. It is not fair to demand confidentiality from a participant and then not be willing to accept help.

4. I will not discuss past suicidal behaviors or the details of my traumas with other participants outside of sessions. This information can be shared with an individual therapist.

5. If I feel overwhelmed, feel at risk for using drugs or alcohol, or feel at risk for self-harm, then I am expected to ask for help.

6. I agree to respect the purpose of this group. This is a structured group designed to teach new skills. This is not a group to process life difficulties or other emotional issues that are not directly related to the class.

7. I agree that if I feel overwhelmed or upset about the group, I will communicate directly to the leader (not just complain to other people in the group).

8. I agree to let the leader know if I need to miss a class for any reason.

9. I agree to speak to members of the group with respect. In other words, nobody is allowed to attack, blame, or curse at other members of the group or the group leader.

10. I agree to allow the leader to lead the group. If the leader has to interrupt, change a topic, or move the group along, I agree to allow the group to move forward.

11. I agree to not eat food/snacks/candy, chew gum, drink caffeinated beverages, or engage in distracting behaviors such as texting, tapping on the table, or knitting during the group.

12. I agree to keep the rules of the group and participate in class discussions.

13. I agree that the group leader can determine if someone needs to be asked to leave the group.

I have read the above agreements and I agree to abide by these rules.

_____

Signed   **Date**

Agreements for the Leader of the Group

1. The leader of this group agrees to start and end the group on time.
2. The leader agrees to provide leadership, lessons, and compassion.
3. The leader agrees to manage the group so it stays on track.
4. The leader agrees to keep the information discussed in this group confidential within the limits of the law. If the leader is a mandated reporter of the state in which this group is being held, then the leader agrees to review the laws of confidentiality.
5. The leader agrees to encourage learning in a safe and fair environment.

As in any course geared for change, you will always get out of it what you put into it. The following are suggested guidelines to maximize your results.

1. *Attend all classes and read all chapters.* This may sound obvious, but in fact it is an essential factor in order to get results. Skipping a chapter means skipping vital lessons and skills. If you are using this book in a class, then class time is valuable to get new information, engage in discussions, provide and receive support, and to keep you motivated and involved in the change process.

2. *Practice the techniques you learn between class sessions.* Practicing the suggested weekly exercises helps build new and healthy habits.

3. *Focus on your own program.* Do your best to make this treatment a priority in your life—the time goes quickly and this is *your* time. That doesn't make you a selfish person, but rather allows you to be a better you, which ultimately helps everyone around you. Also, be careful about getting caught up in other people's issues—their issues are not your responsibility. Remind yourself to focus on your own healing without getting distracted.

Name three things you hope to gain by taking this course.

1. _____

2. _____

3. _____

Name two ways in which you might feel differently after taking this course.

1. _____

2. _____

JOINING THE MILITARY

Name at least one reason why you joined the military.

_____

Name one positive thing you gained by joining the military.

_____

Why do people join the military? Perhaps it's a family tradition or an opportunity to gain new opportunities, participate in something meaningful, or help others . . . why did you join? For whatever reason, you joined for the right reasons—with hope, determination, and excitement. You may have had some amazing experiences beyond what you could have imagined. You may have pushed yourself and accomplished more than you thought was possible. Whatever you experienced, you took a stand to serve. How has the military changed you for the better? Even if your experience did not turn out the way you expected it, and, needless to say, nobody expects to have sexual trauma, you still joined. We will discuss in detail the issues related to sexual trauma, but for now, it is important to acknowledge that you did something pretty incredible: You raised your hand to serve. And for that alone, you should be proud! Thank you for your service, on behalf of all of the citizens in your country.

Nothing can diminish the honor of volunteering to serve one's country.

Now, it is your time . . . time for you to heal.

What Is Military Sexual Trauma?

Although the world is full of suffering, it is also full of the overcoming of it.
—*Helen Keller*

- *Opening exercises: Names and building safety*
  (Day 1: Adjective name memory game, Day 2: Concentration name game)
- *Closing exercises: Signal and cleansing breaths*
  (Day 1: Signal breath, Day 2: Cleansing breath and relaxation sandwich)

SEXUAL TRAUMA

In this course, we define *sexual trauma* as anything that happened or was threatened to happen that was experienced as a violation of a sexual nature. This definition covers a broad range of events that ultimately is defined by the person who experienced the event. More specifically, this may include experiencing or witnessing verbal and nonverbal sexual harassment such as demeaning, inappropriate, and sexualized comments leading to feelings of fear, distrust, and/or being disrespected. It also includes any type of physical touching or other activity of a sexual nature that is against your will or done without your consent. For example, if you are passed out from using alcohol or drugs (legal or illegal), or if you are asleep or otherwise unconscious, by definition your ability to consent to a sexual act is compromised. Sexual trauma also includes unwanted pressure for dates or sex with or without subtle or overt threats. Sexual trauma may include an attempted or completed physical sexual assault, or it may include an ongoing series of events, threats, or unwanted sexual interactions. It may also include a power difference where the abuser is using power to intimidate or control another person, or using trickery, lies, and manipulation. Part of the sexual trauma may be getting the victim to participate, cooperate, or unknowingly walk into a trap. Sexual trauma happens to both men and women, of all ages, ethnicities, and socioeconomic classes.

Some people believe that if they were violated in some way but not actually raped, then their experiences "do not count." Others feel that they may be responsible for the event because they agreed to go on a date, got into someone's car, had a drink, helped a friend, and so forth . . . therefore, whatever happened was "their fault, so it doesn't count." Some may feel that because their bodies responded to the activity it doesn't count as trauma. Others worry that if they didn't fight, scream, or protest it doesn't count. So then why do they have recurring symptoms of distress? Why do they have nightmares and feel embarrassed, guilty, ashamed, weak, terrified to go outside, and/or afraid to trust others? People may feel frustrated and ashamed for having symptoms and wonder why they can't just "snap out of it." Others may also discount or ignore their feelings and wonder why they just "can't get over it."

The reality is all of these events "count" and the fact that people have these types of normal distressing reactions is actually part of the sexual trauma! All of the above incidents describe unwanted sexual encounters or threats that occurred against your will, regardless of whether you fought, screamed, or had a physical sexual response. Sexual trauma occurs in many different forms and any sexual trauma can be deeply wounding, requiring new skills for healing.

YOU ARE NOT ALONE

If you have experienced sexual trauma, you are not alone. In fact, studies show that the numbers are disturbingly high. It is impossible to get an accurate number of exactly how many men, women, and children are sexually abused every year. Most events are never reported, and even if someone musters the courage to report, many cases are dismissed as having insufficient evidence. However, there have been numerous studies surveying thousands of people to estimate the prevalence of sexual trauma. But even with all of this data it is difficult to have a true estimate since people use different definitions of sexual trauma and many people don't feel safe to disclose what has happened to them.

Nonetheless, we can look at these studies and see if there is a trend across them. Even if these estimates are low, it gives us a range of numbers to begin to determine the extent of the issue. Among civilian women, it is estimated that approximately 30% experience some type of sexual trauma in their lifetime. The number for men is about 10% (Resnick, Kilpatrick, Dansky, Saunders, & Best, 1993); this is extremely concerning and far beyond what would be considered an epidemic. Even more concerning is that these numbers are significantly higher for men and women serving in the military.

MILITARY SEXUAL TRAUMA

Military sexual trauma, often called "MST," refers to experiences of sexual trauma that occur while a person is serving on active duty military service. The Department of Veterans Affairs defines MST as "sexual harassment that is threatening in character or physical assault of a sexual nature that occurred while the victim was in the military, regardless of geographic location of the trauma, gender of the victim, or the relationship to the perpetrator." This can include offensive remarks; unwanted sexual touching, grabbing, or threatening; and harassing or unwelcome sexual advances.

A review of 21 studies found MST rates of sexual harassment from 55% to 70% and rates of sexual assault from 11% to 48% among women veterans (Goldzweig, Balekian, Rolon, Yano, & Shekelle, 2006). A review of 25 studies found MST rates of sexual assault ranging from 20% to 43% among women veterans (Suris & Lind, 2008). One of the 25 studies reported a lower rate (0.4%) and another study reported a higher rate (71%). In the Suris and Lind (2008) review, eight studies included men. Seven reported MST rates between 1% and 4% and one study reported 12%. None of the studies reviewed by Suris and Lind (2008) included verbal sexual harassment or unwanted sexual advances, which have been associated with higher rates of MST (Goldzweig et al., 2006). A Department of Defense study (2006) found 16% of men reported MST.

MST has also occurred in the recent conflicts in Iraq and Afghanistan. Kimmerling et al. (2010) and Haskell et al. (2010) examined MST rates among veterans who served in these wars, utilizing the centralized medical records of the Veterans Health Administration. They found approximately 14% to 15.1% of women and 0.7% to 1% of men reported MST when they were screened by health care professionals at their respective VA medical centers. However, Katz, Cojucar, Beheshti, Nakamura, and Murray (2012) examined a diverse sample of these veterans using completely anonymous self-report questionnaires and found rates of MST of 42% for women and 12.5% for men. MST was related to symptoms of posttraumatic stress disorder (PTSD), and in the Katz et al. (2012) study MST was also associated with readjustment difficulties, most strongly with *intimacy problems*.

These studies suggest that MST occurs at a much higher rate than sexual trauma does among civilian populations. It also suggests that when given anonymous questionnaires reports of MST could be even higher than what some studies have found. However, on an encouraging note, in April 2012, Secretary of Defense Panetta made an official public statement that the issue of MST will be addressed throughout the US military. The intention is to launch a series of new policies to improve the investigation and prosecution of the perpetrators of MST. As of today, this is still a work in progress. However, with increased public awareness, the hope is that MST will be recognized, addressed, stopped, and prevented.

What do you think of these numbers? Do these reports seem low, high, or accurate to you and why?

_____

_____

WHY IS SEXUAL TRAUMA HIGHER IN THE MILITARY?

The exact reason why MST is so high is not known and most likely is due to several factors. For one, it may be related to the fact that people in the military are trained in aggression, yet have few outlets for discharging these feelings. It is readily acknowledged that serving in the military may involve managing high pressure and increased stress and frustrations, handling life-threatening situations, dealing with losses without time to grieve, and functioning in a strict and rigid hierarchy that may or may not be perceived as fair or safe. In addition, there is a high use of alcohol in the military, which may impair people's judgment. However, these factors may not explain the high rates in themselves and are certainly not excuses for perpetrating sexual trauma against a fellow service member.

While the military is about serving one's country with honor, and the majority of service men and women are highly respectable and brave, the few who perpetrate on others disgrace the rest of the military. However, certain subcultural factors also exist that may enable behaviors leading to increased MST. For example, because of the strict hierarchy, some people may feel a sense of entitlement over lower-ranking people. Forced sex may be viewed as a form of hazing or an act of domination to inflate one's sense of self-importance or power. Finally, sexual trauma may be seen as a relatively minor issue compared to war or other emergency situations.

Additionally, the military draws upon a diverse population consisting of men and women from a broad range of backgrounds. People enter the military in many different states of mind, and may have had a premilitary trauma history—or possibly a premilitary history of perpetrating sexual trauma.

COMPLICATIONS OF MST

One significant complication of MST is that, unlike civilian trauma, when trauma occurs in the military, people must continue to live and work on base, often with their perpetrator, friends of the perpetrator, or the chain of command of the perpetrator. This creates a hostile environment where there may be a threat of it happening again—undermining people's trust, safety, and ability to function in an optimal way.

Another complication is that when people volunteer to serve in the military, they expect to be challenged, they expect that they could participate in a war, and they train for battle and emergencies . . . but they do not volunteer to be sexually traumatized. One study found that service members are four times more likely to get PTSD from sexual trauma than from combat (Fontana & Ronsenheck, 1998). There may be several reasons for this finding. First, combat trauma is impersonal, whereas MST is a very personal experience. Combat is acknowledged by others, while MST is minimized and silenced. In addition, service members train for and expect to be confronted with bombings and killings associated with combat. However, nobody expects to be attacked by a fellow service member, especially not by someone who is known, trusted, or part of one's military family.

REPORTING SEXUAL TRAUMA

Another complication of MST is the issue of reporting what happened. Did you report MST? Unfortunately, only a small minority of people report and fewer yet feel that swift, satisfying action was taken. Most people do not report MST at all, and others that do report maybe wished they hadn't. And yet, years later, survivors may harbor guilt for not reporting, thinking that maybe their report could have saved someone else, or maybe they would feel less frustrated and powerless if they "did something." However, if you did or didn't report it, there were probably many good reasons why. How do you think the report would have been received? With support, empathy, and concern? Or would you have been mocked, blamed, and punished? What do you think would have been the outcome?

Many people fear that reporting would have made things a lot worse. For example, people may be hesitant to report MST or seek treatment for fear of having it affect their career, or they may need to rely on others who may like or support the perpetrator, including in battle, for promotions, or for other services. They may fear being blamed, ostracized, seen as weak, not being believed, or becoming the topic of vicious gossip. They also may fear retaliation or further abuse from others such as being seen as an "easy target" or as someone who is disrupting unit cohesion. In other words, victims may be afraid to "rock the boat" and tend not to say anything. They already feel vulnerable and afraid. So instead of taking the risk of reporting or seeking treatment, they end up "suffering in silence." This intensifies the feelings of embarrassment and shame. Some MST survivors choose not to tell anyone and keep this secret inside of them for many years.

SEXUAL TRAUMA AND MEN

Sexual trauma that happens to men is often minimized. It is embarrassing for men and may call into question their manhood and their ability to fend for themselves. They have to fight against a male sexual stereotype that "men always want to have sex"—so how could they have unwanted sex, sexual attention, or be traumatized? This, of course, is not the case and sexual trauma for men is equally as violating as it is for women. As with women, most perpetrators (but not all) are heterosexual (straight) men. If the trauma is perpetrated from a man to another man, it has no bearing on the perpetrator's or recipient's sexual orientation. Acts of sexual trauma are not about sex, but rather are about domination, control, and violence. Similar as with women, the arousal is from power and not sexual attraction. Men can be the recipient of unwanted verbal comments, physical advances, or acts of rape from a man or woman, gay or straight.

In addition, an act of sexual trauma between people of the same gender does not change someone's sexual orientation. Your orientation before the trauma is still your orientation after the trauma. This can be very confusing, especially if you are a man who had a sexual response to the event. But just because the body responds to stimulation does not negate or minimize the trauma. Sexual trauma is demeaning, humiliating, and terrifying for anyone, either male or female, who experiences it, regardless of whether the perpetrator was a man or woman. However, men are less likely to admit, disclose, or report sexual trauma, and are less likely to seek help than women. Men are also more likely to worry about their sexual identity. Although both men and women can have difficulties engaging in or desiring sex following sexual trauma, men tend to feel more pressure and distress because of this.

UNDERSTANDING SEXUAL ASSAULTS

How does sexual assault happen and who are the perpetrators? The stereotype of a perpetrator of sexual assault is some sort of creepy, scary "boogeyman" lurking in a dark alley, wearing a ski mask, and holding a gun or knife. This image is consistent with what our society thinks of as a "perpetrator" and it is what is typically portrayed in movies and television shows. In addition, much of the early research found that perpetrators fit this image. The problem with that research is that they only surveyed those who were caught and put in prison. It is estimated that this stereotype only represents about 5% of perpetrators. Since the majority of cases are never reported, the majority of perpetrators are never adjudicated, never convicted by juries, and 95% are never sent to prison. One thing we have been able to find in subsequent research studies is that the majority of perpetrators of sexual assault are not scary strangers but rather are people who know their victims and whom other people respect and trust. They may seem like "nice" people, be successful in their careers, have families, and otherwise be upstanding trustworthy citizens!

If this seems inconsistent and confusing, then you are right. Because most perpetrators do not fit the stereotype of a man in a ski mask lurking in a dark alley, others have difficulty understanding or believing what happened. Perpetrators of sexual assault often use trickery to perform their acts and rely on being sneaky to get away with it. They may work hard to gain the trust of others. But, of course, they are anything but nice and are certainly not trustworthy. Perpetrators know what they are doing. Whether the assault is opportunistic or premeditated, perpetrators have to consciously work to set up their victims, acting in a calculating way.

People who hear about sexual assault can't make sense of it and may end up blaming the one reporting the event because they think of the perpetrator as "such a nice guy." This confusion between who the perpetrator is to other people (in public, at work, in the military, or to other family members) and who the perpetrator is behind closed doors is one of the reasons why experiences of sexual trauma do not get reported, do not get prosecuted, and why other people may not believe what happened. This is incredibly frustrating and hurtful to victims of sexual trauma—and also one reason memories do not get processed well and remain stuck as painful and unresolved.

Remembering sexual trauma and its perpetrators can provoke strong, mixed feelings. On the one hand, it is common to feel duped and tricked. On the other hand, it is natural to feel fury, even years later—thinking, "How DARE they!" It is equally aggravating to think the perpetrator got away with it or, worse yet, that others actually blame the victim for it! And, of course, worst of all, the victim (or survivor) may even blame him- or herself for it.

In this course, you will examine what happened to you as an objective observer like a newspaper reporter (looking at the facts) or a scientist (examining the evidence in an objective manner) to help you understand the truth or multiple layers of the truth. The goal is to process your thoughts about the trauma so that you can see the whole picture, feel validated, make sense of it, put blame where blame is due, and then finally move past the past and into a more hopeful future.

NORMAL REACTIONS TO SEXUAL TRAUMA

What is "normal" when it comes to responding to sexual trauma? Everyone experiences sexual trauma differently, and there is a wide range of responses and symptoms in response to trauma. Biological predisposition, the nature of the trauma, supportive aftercare, and other factors all play a role in a person's reaction to trauma and the extent of resulting symptoms.

In addition, an event of trauma may not be the extent of distress, as trauma is rarely, if ever, really a single event. Even a single act of sexual trauma has many aftereffects such as the struggle of whether or not to report it, how the report is handled, to whom the trauma is disclosed, how it is received, and the potential multitude of symptoms that may have occurred. Some aftereffects—for example, being blamed, not believed, and minimized; feeling betrayed by family or friends; or having to deal with life-altering changes such as contracting a disease, having a debilitating injury, losing a career, losing a significant relationship, or contending with an unwanted pregnancy—may be even more devastating than the initial event of trauma. These are called "secondary traumas" and may need treatment just as much as primary traumas.

Common Symptoms After MST

MST can manifest in a multitude of symptoms affecting every aspect of one's life—from emotional, psychological, behavioral, and physical issues to finances, relationships, legal issues, and homelessness.

Emotional issues may include feeling depressed, sad, hurt, grief-stricken, empty, and lost; anxious, terrified, nervous, insecure, vulnerable, and overwhelmed; angry, resentful, bitter, and furious; ashamed, embarrassed, guilty, and self-hating; or numb, flat, disengaged, and withdrawn. Emotional issues may also include feeling "triggered" or having sudden experiences of anxiety due to a recall of an aspect of the trauma. You might have experienced all of these symptoms and many more not on this list.

Psychological symptoms include negative thought patterns such as negative thinking about "all men" or "all women"; negative thoughts around trust, safety, and self-blame; and recurrent worries such as "I should have . . . ," "I could have . . . ," and "I would have. . . ." These may all be part of a sexual trauma survivor's thoughts years after the event.

Some behavioral problems associated with sexual trauma include substance abuse (e.g., alcohol and drug use) and other addictions as a way of escaping from the thoughts and feelings of the trauma, eating disorders, difficulty in relationships, difficulty keeping a job, self-injury, isolation from others, and not complying with treatment. Other behavioral issues may be nightmares, poor sleep, and insomnia.

Physical problems associated with sexual trauma may include immune system dysfunctions, gynecological problems, HIV or other sexually transmitted diseases, sexual dysfunction, and issues with reproductive health. Some survivors may experience memory loss, an inability to retrieve memories, or an inability to concentrate. Many survivors of MST have multiple health problems, chronic illnesses, and chronic pain.

This is not an exhaustive list but is presented to show the broad array of symptoms following sexual trauma. Can you see how the accumulation of symptoms leads to more problems that lead to more symptoms?

Homelessness and MST

Homelessness among veterans is a growing concern, particularly for women veterans who are three to four times more likely to become homeless than nonveteran women (Gamache, Rosenheck, & Tessler, 2003). The link between MST and homelessness is a perfect example of accumulated symptoms. What if a survivor is having so many symptoms that it is too difficult to keep a job? Then the bills start piling up, leading to increased negative thinking and feelings of being overwhelmed. What if the survivor doesn't have supportive friends and doesn't have the energy or self-esteem to make friends? What if the survivor doesn't have a supportive family?

Unfortunately, people can feel completely isolated and alone, overwhelmed by external and internal stress, and unable to sleep or stop the racing thoughts that can lead to an increased desire for substance abuse or escape (e.g., through addictions, self-injury, and even suicide). What if the only solution is to get into a relationship, or stay on a friend's couch, but then that turns into an abusive situation? Unfortunately, it is not surprising that, with compounding difficulties and without resources, female veterans with MST, unemployment, poor health, and PTSD are at high risk for homelessness (Washington et al., 2010).

> There are half hours that dilate to the importance of centuries.
> —*Mary Catherwood*

Did You Know . . .

According to the National Institutes of Health, PTSD affects some 7.7 million Americans. Women are more likely than men to develop PTSD. In fact, recent studies have shown that women experience PTSD at a rate twice that of men.

POSTTRAUMATIC STRESS DISORDER

About 30% of people who experience sexual trauma develop PTSD at some point during their lifetime. Sexual trauma and torture are the two types of events most likely to lead to PTSD. Why do you think that is? _____

_____

PTSD occurs when a person has been exposed to an event that involved possible injury or death, and which resulted in feelings of intense fear, helplessness, or horror. Years after the event, the person may continue to experience a variety of responses and feelings that he or she didn't have before the event. These include nightmares; avoiding people, places, and things; a sense of panic; irritability; anxiety; and an intense feeling of being unsafe resulting in hyper-awareness of anything that could possibly be dangerous. People who have PTSD may have flashbacks to the traumatic episode, feeling as if it is happening all over again. This feeling can occur unexpectedly or in response to something that might remind the person of the event.

People who have experienced trauma may feel overwhelmed by the experience and want to avoid thoughts, feelings, places, people, or anything else that might remind them of the trauma. They might also choose to avoid crowds or social situations, withdrawing from other people, and lose interest in doing the things that were once sources of pleasure. Many people with PTSD are unable to recall some important elements of the experience while also having recurrent thoughts of other parts of the experience. They may also have negative thinking about themselves or others.

Even people who don't meet the full criteria for PTSD are not necessarily free of symptoms. Sexual trauma can affect many aspects of a person's life and all of these responses are normal and typical responses. Not only are they normal, typical, and common reactions, but they are also *treatable.* It is very important to know that you CAN heal from MST. Many people do . . . and so can you! You are using this workbook because you want to and deserve to heal. Stay with the course (show up even when you don't feel like it!) and let the experience help you resolve the past and move forward in your life in a positive way.

FOUR THINGS TO CONSIDER WHEN HEALING FROM MST

1. It is normal to feel upset when you read about MST and consider how it has affected your life. These feelings make sense, are justified . . . and will change. As you heal, the intense feelings of distress may become less frequent, less intense, and may not last as long. Instead of judging your experience, consider telling yourself, *"It's okay, I'm healing,"* every time you have an episode of intense feelings during the program. They will pass.

2. Each traumatic experience is different, but many people have similar responses to experiencing sexual trauma. In other words, YOU ARE NOT ALONE. Breaking the silence about your trauma can help in the healing process. An important part of this course is recognizing that others share similarities to your experience—and may share important insights to support you in your healing.

3. It's also reassuring to know that you have had and are having a normal reaction to trauma. Even if other people in the room react differently, it is all normal and makes sense. Some people shut down and cannot express themselves, while others become bold and are quick to defend themselves from any abuser or form of danger. Both responses are coping strategies in order to be safe. Whatever your response to trauma, it developed for a good reason.

4. Finally, when embarking on this journey it is important to remember to have compassion for yourself and for others in the room. Everyone, including you, is trying to cope.

Writing exercise: How has past trauma affected your life? Consider your health, family, career, finances, emotional well-being, and lifestyle.

Writing exercise: **What would you like to change or be different as you move forward into the future? Consider your health, family, career, finances, emotional well-being, and lifestyle.**

_____

_____

_____

_____

_____

_____

_____

_____

_____

_____

_____

_____

_____

_____

_____

_____

_____

_____

_____

_____

_____

CHAPTER 1 SUMMARY POINTS

- This book defines sexual trauma as anything that occurred or was threatened to occur that was experienced as a violation of a sexual nature. The Department of Veterans Affairs defines MST as "sexual harassment that is threatening in character or physical assault of a sexual nature that occurred while the victim was in the military, regardless of geographic location of the trauma, gender of the victim, or the relationship to the perpetrator."

- You are not alone: It is estimated that 30% of women and 10% of men experience sexual trauma, and in the military rates of MST are as high as 55% for women and 12% for men!

- MST may include further complications for sexual trauma survivors since they are "captive" by the military, requiring them to continue to live and work with their perpetrator and friends of the perpetrator.

- Sexual assaults are typically enacted by perpetrators who premeditate and plan their attacks using trickery, lies, and manipulation.

- Normal reactions to sexual trauma include anger, anxiety, panic attacks (or a sense of feeling overwhelmed), shame, guilt, self-blame, substance abuse and other addictions, running away, depression, and even self-harm.

MST happens. It is not your fault. Your symptoms are normal . . .
AND you can heal!

THIS WEEK'S CLOSING EXERCISES (SEE APPENDIX B)

At the end of class on the first day, review and practice the *signal breath*. At the end of class on the second day, review and practice the *cleansing breath*. Then practice them together using the *relaxation sandwich*.

Signal Breath

The *signal breath* is one of the most versatile relaxation skills. It is quick and easy to do. It literally takes 5 seconds! It can be used when you feel angry, frustrated, or afraid. It is called a *signal breath* because, like a traffic signal, it helps you slow down, stop . . . and then move forward in a more relaxed frame of mind. It is based on two principles: (1) you can't be relaxed and tense at the same time (e.g., your hand is either open or in a fist), and (2) everything is connected . . . so if you relax your mind, then you also relax your body, and if you relax your body, then you relax your mind. So in this exercise, the idea is to hold the breath, building up tension, and then when you release the breath, you experience relaxation.

It goes like this: Take in a deep breath, inhaling through your nose. Hold it at the top for several seconds (up to 5 seconds if that's comfortable for you). Then, let it out slowly through your mouth. As you exhale, imagine all of the tension leaving your body.

Cleansing Breath

The *cleansing breath* is probably the simplest technique in this book but yields impressive results. Imagine the breath is like taking a shower or standing under a cleansing waterfall—washing all the tension away. Do not hold the breath during this exercise. It is designed to be a quick "cleanse." It can be used anywhere or any time when you want a quick release of tension.

It goes like this: Take a deep breath in through the nose and let it out with a heavy sigh. Try this without the sigh and then with the sigh—feel the difference?

Relaxation Sandwich

The *relaxation sandwich* starts with the *signal breath* and ends with the *cleansing breath*. The two breaths are the "bread" and any other closing exercise is the filing. This sandwich technique will be used throughout *Warrior Renew* as a way to begin and end a relaxation session. Start with two to three *signal breaths*, then a single or series of closing exercises, and end with two to three *cleansing breaths*.

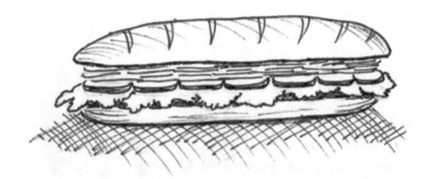

Coping With Feelings

2

Breathe. Let go. And remind yourself that this very moment is the only one you know you have for sure.
—*Oprah Winfrey*

- *Opening exercises: Movement and building safety
  (Day 1: Water molecule, Day 2: Groupings)*
- *Closing exercises: Relaxation skills
  (Day 1: Body scan and emotional scan, Day 2: Biofeedback machine and decoding your feelings—using the relaxation sandwich for both days)*

FEELINGS . . .?

Most people want to avoid negative feelings and run away from the topic as fast as they can. In addition, as a military warrior you have been trained to put your personal feelings aside, focus on your job, and focus on the mission. Feelings were not important and considered a disruption of service, weak, and inappropriate. Instead, you were encouraged to "be strong," "be tough," and certainly "not feel."

So what happened after the MST? It would make perfect sense if you took all of your feelings, stuffed them in a box, taped it shut, and buried them in a remote cave deep inside of yourself—never to see daylight again. It's a tricky situation: On the one hand you want to heal from MST and be free of the tension caused by this pent up issue, and on the other hand . . . you most likely don't want to open up that box! Even the idea of finding the box can be quite distressing. What is inside of the box? Maybe there is one intense feeling or a mixture of several feelings (e.g., anger, sadness, and fear) or maybe you are afraid there is nothing in there at all. What if you open the box and you can't control or stop the feelings? Maybe you will be so upset that you'll start to cry, maybe you won't be able to stop crying, or maybe you'll be so angry that you will explode or say or do something you regret. The fear of opening the box is acknowledging that there are strong and powerful feelings in there and you are not sure what to do with them. It is normal to be skeptical about the box of feelings, and therefore it would make sense if your feelings were boxed up, avoided, and pushed aside. So for now, let's *not* open that box, at least not until we explore what feelings are, what they are not, and how to understand their true power.

While it is perfectly normal to want to avoid anything that is uncomfortable, such as intense negative feelings, what can happen if feelings are completely avoided? Can you see how avoiding negative emotions leads to avoiding all emotions? And if taken to an extreme, avoidance can jeopardize one's health, relationships, and general well-being?

Can you think of three ways that avoiding emotions can take a toll on your health, relationships, and general well-being?

1. _____

2. _____

3. _____

SOME COMMON AVOIDANCE STRATEGIES

What avoidance strategies do you use when feelings become too much or uncomfortable? Below is a list of common but generally unhealthy strategies. Do any of these apply to you?

1. **Addictions**: substance abuse, smoking, gambling, overspending, overeating

2. **Numbing distraction:** sleeping, watching TV, playing video games, using the computer

3. **Chaos distraction**: frequent crises, fights, and emergencies

4. **Physical distancing**: quitting jobs, moving, canceling appointments, running away

5. **Mental lapses**: forgetfulness, memory lapses, confusion, difficulty concentrating

6. **Social avoidance**: ending relationships, isolating oneself, withdrawing socially, cheating or creating reasons for someone to leave (pushing others away), avoiding sexual intimacy

7. **Self-injury**: not complying with medications, over- or undereating, bingeing on sugary or salty foods, cutting oneself, attempting suicide, entering destructive relationships, having unprotected sex, engaging in reckless behavior, seeking an adrenalin rush (e.g., thrill seeking, practicing extreme sports, shoplifting)

8. **Depression:** feeling numb, "shut down," tired, unmotivated, indecisive

9. **Anxiety:** feeling jittery, tense; can't sit still; being spacey, scattered, unfocused; using caffeine

THE MEANING OF FEELINGS

While it may have been adaptive in the military to avoid feelings, the fact is you are a human being and, as such, are physiologically wired to feel. Feelings are actually adaptive. Ironically, instead of making you "weak," feelings can give you important information and if understood properly can make you "strong," "wise," and "successful."

How you view feelings has a large impact on how you experience and cope with them.

In this chapter, feelings will be *redefined* from something that may be unwanted or dreaded to something that is *useful*. In this way, instead of avoiding negative emotions such as feeling hurt, angry, or afraid, you can welcome them. Once they are seen as useful information, they can help you feel more empowered and in control. (Imagine that!)

The truth is, feelings are powerful tools of communication. They are the body's way of expressing vital information about a situation. For example, let's say you were camping and you heard a loud roar. Your body is wired to have an emotional reaction: your heart starts racing, your muscles become tense, and you gasp for air. You are feeling fear. And it is this reaction that helps protect you against a potential danger.

All feelings communicate important information. What do you think emotions of anger, sadness, and joy communicate? What do they tell you about a situation? How could these feelings be *beneficial*? For example, when you feel angry, what is going on that triggers anger inside of you? Maybe there was an injustice, a violation, or a thwarted expectation? The voice inside of you may be saying, "Hey, that is not supposed to happen!" and it makes you feel angry.

Information from feelings helps people make empowering and productive choices. Awareness of feelings allows people to evaluate themselves and the situation. If people are unaware of their feelings (i.e., what they are feeling and why they are feeling it), they run the risk of reacting to situations impulsively, inappropriately, or destructively. Have you ever had a time when you reacted to a situation because your emotions were extremely intense and then later realized you had reacted too soon or regretted your response? What might have happened differently if you first tried to understand your feelings instead of just reacting to them?

Not only do feelings communicate useful information about a specific situation, they also provide information about underlying thought patterns. Feelings are the gateway to the unconscious mind. Paying attention to feelings may help reveal underlying unresolved issues. For example, Leonard had a response of extreme sadness to a situation of a minor loss. When he wrote about his feelings, he became aware of similar feelings that he had in childhood. He realized that he carried unresolved grief related to his grand-mother's death when he was 6 years old, and later his parents' divorce when he was 8 years old. The current loss allowed him to recognize and address the feelings he had buried from his past. He also became aware of his associated thoughts that "everyone he loves leaves him." Once he realized what he was thinking, he was able to understand where it was coming from and evaluate that it wasn't completely true (e.g., not *everyone* he loves leaves).

Feelings link memories of similar feelings together. If something makes you feel sad, other memories of sadness will be easier to retrieve. If something makes you feel angry, other memories of anger will be easier to retrieve. For example, imagine a string of holiday lights. The string represents a specific type of emotion such as "depression." Each lightbulb represents an event where you felt depressed. If a new event occurs that triggers depression, all the other events are more easily remembered. It is as if the new event plugs in the string of holiday lights and all of the lightbulbs light up! This explains why sometimes you may have intense feelings from a relatively minor experience. It also explains why when you work on healing one incident it also helps heal the whole string of lights.

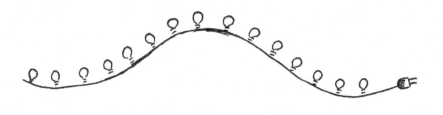

FEELINGS COME FROM OUR THOUGHTS

Feelings come from our thoughts and mental images. It is impossible to have a feeling without a thought. The thought can either be in our awareness (a conscious thought) or outside of our awareness (an unconscious thought). Conscious thoughts are slow and deliberate. It is the type of thinking that occurs when you work on figuring out a problem, mull over a decision, recall something that has happened, or think about a conversation with someone. By thinking about it, you may slowly come to realize how you feel about it. A feeling may grow as you continue to think about it and generate mental images.

In contrast, thoughts from the unconscious mind are fast, automatic, and outside of our awareness. An example of an unconscious thought is the quick, instant judgment that we make in a potentially dangerous situation. If you recognize that something dangerous could happen, such as seeing a ladder falling toward you, your mind quickly assesses the situation and mobilizes you to run, fight, or freeze. Afterward, you may experience signs of an "adrenalin rush" such as a racing heart rate; fast, shallow breathing; and a feeling of fear and exhilaration. If you waited for your conscious mind to think about the situation, such as taking the time to calculate the relative danger and assessing your options for action, the ladder would have already fallen!

We can also have unconscious thoughts when we make instant judgments about situations or other people. We may not be aware of why we feel a certain way, but at an unconscious level a determination has been made. Maybe something triggers a memory from the past and you are not aware of it. You may all of a sudden have anxiety or feeling of panic—but nothing happened. At some level, you had an unconscious thought of danger and your body responded. Feelings come from our thoughts. They are not generated externally. They don't happen to us. Feelings don't invade us like a virus. Feelings are responses to our own conscious and unconscious mind. Pay attention to your feelings and you will see what your mind is thinking. If you have a chronic feeling, then you are working on regenerating it. You may be focusing on something that happened or on a particular image. The feeling will come from your thoughts.

You can't have a feeling unless your mind is generating a thought!

What thoughts are associated with each of these feelings?
For example: Anger may be generated from thoughts that something is not fair or is not right.

Anger _____

Fear _____

Sadness _____

Disgust _____

Rage _____

Despair _____

Shame _____

Apprehension _____

Anxiety _____

Peace _____

Here are some associated thoughts to the above feelings:

Fear = thoughts that something could be dangerous

Sadness = thoughts about missing someone/something, thoughts of a loss

Disgust = thoughts of something repulsive

Rage = thoughts about something extremely unjust

Despair = thoughts of being hopeless

Shame = thoughts of embarrassment, self-disapproval

Apprehension = thoughts of uncertainty and potential discomfort

Anxiety = thoughts of worry, anticipating poor outcomes

Peace = thoughts of safety and well-being

What other feelings can you think of and what thoughts do those feelings tell you?

_____

_____

The body is an instrument of the unconscious and conscious mind. It responds to our thoughts. If you think about something that upsets you, you will feel upset. If you think about something that is not fair or just, you will most likely feel angry. If you think about something dear to you that you lost, you will most likely feel sad. Similarly, if you think about something that you enjoy—walking on the beach or laughing with a friend—how will you feel?

Thoughts → feelings
Identifying your feelings → identifying your thoughts

FEELINGS ARE PHYSICAL SENSATIONS

It is impossible to have a feeling without experiencing it in the body. People may not be aware that feelings are sensations and may be confused or uncomfortable by the experience. Because of this lack of awareness, for some people, the sensations of feelings trigger fear of being overwhelmed and out of control. One task in learning how to manage and tolerate feelings is to become aware and more comfortable with the physical sensations associated with each feeling.

What physical sensations are associated with feelings? For the following exercise, imagine that you are experiencing each of the feelings written below (one at a time!). How does each one feel in your body? Do certain places feel tense, heavy, or energized? Do you notice changes in your facial expression? Are some easier or more difficult than others? What do you notice? You may want to close your eyes and imagine feeling each one.

What sensations are associated with each of these feelings? Can you detect subtle differences between the various feelings?
For example: Anger may be experienced as tension in the jaw, forehead, neck, shoulders, arms, and fists as well as increased temperature and heart rate; quickened, shallow breathing; and lots of energy to fight or scream.

Fear _____

Sadness _____

Disgust _____

Rage _____

Despair _____

Shame _____

Apprehension _____

Anxiety _____

Peace _____

FEELINGS COME AND THEY GO

Feelings come and they go. They are impermanent, fleeting experiences. Have you ever seen a child cry and then 1 minute later laugh? The child is experiencing feelings without holding onto them—just letting them flow. Feelings are meant to flow through us like water flows through a garden hose. When we hold back the feelings (kink the hose), what happens? Pressure builds up, some water may squirt out and escape, and the hose may feel like it will explode. Similarly, when we hold back our feelings it may feel like we want to explode. Even if you think you shut off the water completely, you may surprise yourself when all of a sudden you explode with emotion. The water is there—it is meant to flow. We are supposed to have emotions and they will effortlessly flow through us if we allow them to do so. They may be intense for a while, but they will dissipate. Feelings come and they go, especially when you let them flow.

Feelings are meant to flow through us like water flows through a garden hose.

FEELINGS ARE RESPONSES, NOT FACTS

Feelings are not facts. They are emotional and physical responses to our thoughts. Of course, people have a right to feel their feelings, but just because they have a feeling doesn't mean that the feeling is right, accurate, or the most adaptive response to a situation. Sometimes people have old feelings surface in response to a current situation. To an outside observer, it may seem that the person's response is too intense for the situation. In this case, the current situation "triggers" old unresolved feelings. For example, John told Jenny he couldn't see her on the weekend because he had promised to help a friend. Jenny yelled at him and said he was a jerk and she "never wanted to see him again!" Her behavior may seem too drastic for the situation but "makes sense" given Jenny's history. The situation with John triggered emotional memories of when she was rejected and abandoned in previous relationships. She was not aware of the reason, but she felt extremely angry. Jenny's feelings were her response to her own experiences and do not necessarily mean that it was a fact that John was going to abandon her, too.

Because people may not be aware of why they feel so strongly about something, they may use their strong feelings to assert control in a situation even when it is not necessary. For example, Henry uses his anger to convince others that he is right and others are wrong. However, just because Henry is angry doesn't make his point more or less true. Feelings do not make something right or true. In another example, some people used to believe that the earth was flat and felt very strongly that a loved one should not sail to "the edge." Just because the emotion is intense does not mean the danger of falling off the earth is real! Sometimes it is confusing because when you feel something so strongly, it seems that whatever the perception is must be true.

On the other hand, feelings *are* an accurate reflection of how each person thinks about a situation. In the previous example, the strong feeling of not wanting someone to sail does not mean the world really is flat, but it does mean that the person really fears losing someone he or she loves. Some situations do warrant strong feelings but those feelings are always a response to a person's thoughts. Those thoughts include a person's opinions, perceptions, judgments, and/or evaluation of a situation. Useful information about your thoughts can be gained by paying attention to your feelings. You can learn what you think about a situation, and you can learn if something in the current situation reminds you of something that is still bothering you from the past. Then you may have more options on how to handle a situation.

FEELINGS ARE PART OF NEURAL NETWORKS

There is nothing more convincing than an emotional experience to reinforce or strengthen the bond between a certain thought and a feeling. You already know the power of a bad experience: One bad experience is enough to convince a person never to do or try something again. This is the body's natural way of learning. A network of neurons in the brain connects anything associated with a particularly intense emotional experience. For example, if you had a bad experience eating string beans, then the thought of string beans will bring up a bad feeling. But if you later taste a wonderful string bean dish, it weakens the association between "string beans and bad feeling," and you may be more open (although skeptical) to trying string beans again. The more positive experiences you have with string beans, the more the old association will weaken and the new association strengthen.

Because an association or neural network has been formed between certain thoughts and feelings, triggering the network can sometimes be used to justify the thoughts and feelings. Consider Donna, who was very certain in her belief that she could not trust anyone because of what happened to her in the military. Her thoughts of distrust reinforce her feelings of anxiety, while her feelings of anxiety reinforce her thoughts of distrust. This is an interesting self-sustaining trap! It wouldn't take much to engage her neural network, thereby strengthening her thoughts and feelings.

What is the solution? Change the thoughts or change the feelings? Either can work as long as Donna *experiences* that she does not need to fear all people. For example, she could have a positive experience in a group and realize that it is possible to feel safe with others. When she feels differently, she may think differently about other people. Or she can convince herself that not *all* people are untrustworthy or out to get her, and thereby become more open to having new experiences with other people. Once Donna has a disconfirming experience (i.e., that she actually can have a positive experience with others leading to increased trust) she will by definition change her thoughts and her feelings!

Example: George asks Mary to go to a party. Mary says, "No thanks; I hate parties." George asks, "Do you hate all parties?" Mary says, "Yep, pretty much." George persists, "Well, would you hate a quiet dinner party with a few friends?" Mary ponders. "Okay, you got me. I don't hate *all* parties." George offers a plan: "Well, this should be a really nice party. We can go together, you can bring another friend, and we can all leave whenever you want. If you don't like it, we'll leave and I'll treat you to dinner—your choice." Mary agrees and they go.

This conversation illustrates that Mary has an association with parties and quickly (without conscious thought) responded, "No thanks; I hate parties," because the party that she thought about in her mind is associated with a bad feeling—most likely based on a bad experience. Although George was able to open up Mary's mind to the possibility of a party that she wouldn't hate, she still holds the bad association in her mind. If George takes her to the party and she has a bad time, it will reinforce her beliefs about parties.

Do you want to go to a party?

Mental image and emotional response	→	No! I hate parties.
Challenging the thought	→	Do you hate all parties? How about a quiet dinner party?
More open thinking	→	No, I don't hate *all* parties.
Behavioral plan	→	We can go together and leave whenever you want.
New experience	→	Okay, let's go to the party.
If she has a *bad* experience	→	Strengthens original association
If she has a *good* experience	→	Weakens original association

If, on the other hand, she has a good time, this new experience will weaken the old association that was based on her past. Positive experiences weaken the bonds associated with a mental image and negative feelings such as fear, anger, and hurt.

Another way to address Mary's declaration that she "hates parties" is to find out *why*. What image is generated when she thinks of "party"? Mary said, "When I think of parties, I think about a loud crowded party. The music is thumping. I see myself in the middle of the dance floor having fun. Then all of a sudden a crowd of people surrounds me on the dance floor and I feel trapped. I can't breathe. Sweaty bodies are closing in on me. . . . I remember a distinct smell."

Then she said, "I know why I don't like parties. They remind me of feeling trapped and out of control. It reminds me of my rape in the military. I couldn't breathe. I never want to feel that way again. That's why I hate parties, even though the rape happened in the back of a truck—isn't that strange?"

In this example, the association with "party" really has nothing to do with parties at all, but rather unresolved issues related to past MST. Of course, Mary never wants to feel that way again. So as a protective mechanism, she simply avoids all potentially uncomfortable situations that may or may not actually be dangerous. However, avoiding new situations is actually counterproductive. It may bring relief in the moment but it fuels the fear and strengthens the negative associations to the past. **If Mary never goes to a party again, she will always be afraid of parties.** New experiences are vital to weakening old negative bonds and strengthening new ones. New experience is how to change the neural networks in your brain!

EXPERIENCE

Experience is the key to permanent and lasting change. So then, what constitutes an experience? Can a thought be an experience? A thought such as "2 + 2 = 4" or "I wonder what I should have for dinner" are just thoughts. However, if you think about having a delicious lasagna for dinner, and you imagine a friend coming over and you are laughing and enjoying the meal, then this would be considered an "imaginal experience." The difference between the first and second types of thoughts is that in the second ones you are having images that evoke emotions and sensations similar to an experience.

There are different types of experience: actual experience (what is experienced in life) and imaginal experience (what is thought about and imagined). Thinking about memories (evoking images from past experience) and thinking about fantasy (evoking images using imagination) are both using imagination. Vicarious experience—watching someone else have an experience and then imagining what that feels like—is also an imaginal experience. This is why you can watch a movie and cry for the actor; you are feeling as though you are part of the experience. Thoughts lead to feelings and feelings can influence thoughts—both of these influence people's behaviors, but it is experience that reinforces patterns of thoughts and feelings. If you want

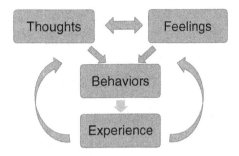

to change—and have lasting permanent change—then new experience is the element that can interrupt old associations and create new neural networks.

However, interventions along any part of this equation will affect the whole equation. For example, you might not have lasagna tonight if you don't first think about what you want for dinner. This is just like in the example with Mary: Once she was more open in her thinking, she was more likely to engage in a new behavior (go to the party), allowing herself to engage in a new experience.

In this class, you will learn more about these neural networks and why you have learned to feel the way that you do. The networks have been formed as an adaptive strategy to help you avoid danger or unpleasant experiences. However, they can also be limiting and prevent you from fully engaging in your life. This will be explained in detail in future chapters. We will also refer to this model of changing thoughts, feelings, and behaviors with the goal of leading to new experiences.

SKILLS TO IDENTIFY AND RELEASE FEELINGS

It is an illusion to think that avoiding feelings keeps you in control. In reality, all it does is keep you from yourself. Your feelings are communications sent from your own mind to your body. Your body decodes these messages and expresses them as feelings. They are indicators of what you sense in any given situation. For example, as we discussed, if you are angry, then you probably sense an injustice. If you are sad, then you probably sense a loss. If you are afraid, then you probably sense danger. It is up to you to listen to your feelings and decipher the message. First we will focus on becoming aware of your breathing and physical state of tension or relaxation. Then we will practice techniques to become aware of and release feelings.

YOUR OWN BIOFEEDBACK MACHINE

Your own *biofeedback machine* is a technique to help you learn the difference between tense breathing and relaxed breathing. *Biofeedback* is a word that means receiving feedback about your biological systems. In this case, the feedback lets you know if you are relaxed or tense. This particular machine is very convenient because (1) it does not need any batteries, (2) it is something you can take with you wherever you go, and (3) it's free! Simply use both of your hands as the sensors to detect information about your body. One hand is placed on the chest and the other is placed on the lower belly. Breathing from the thorax, or the upper part of the chest, is shallow and tense breathing. In comparison, breathing from your diaphragm, or the lower part of your belly, is deep, relaxed breathing.

The Biofeedback Machine Is Practiced Like This

- Place one hand on your upper chest
- Place the other on your belly, just below the belly button
- Watch your hands to get feedback about your breathing

First practice exaggerating your breath to move only your upper hand. This is shallow, tense breathing. Then exaggerate your breath to move only your lower hand. This is relaxed, deep breathing. Then, take one to two *signal breaths* and let yourself relax. Place your hands in the biofeedback positions and observe the movement of your hands as you breathe. As you continue to relax, notice if your hands move differently. Now concentrate on breathing deeply into the belly. Use the feedback from your hands to deepen your relaxed breathing. By breathing slowly and deeply, the breath should naturally move into the lower belly and therefore move the lower hand. This exercise will help you become more aware of your breathing and the sensations associated with being tense versus being relaxed. Don't worry if it seems difficult to control or change your breath, the mere placing of the hands in this position can be comforting and relaxing. Use a gentle approach to help you release the tension in your chest and shoulders, inhaling and focusing on exhaling fully, releasing just a bit more with each cycle of breath.

DECODING YOUR FEELINGS

Awareness of feelings helps you decipher the following questions: (1) What are you feeling? (2) What information does it reveal about the current situation? (3) What information, if any, does it reveal about a past situation? The following exercise adapted from *Journey to Your Heart* (Katz, 2006b) will help you learn how to communicate with your feelings by learning how to listen and decipher the language of feelings through awareness of the sensations in your body. After all, the body is the best tool to know how you feel.

It Is Practiced in Six Steps

1. Getting centered
2. Focusing on sensations in your body
3. Identifying the feelings
4. Decoding the message (that the feeling is communicating)
5. Releasing the feeling and the tension
6. Deciding on your response

Do what you can with this exercise. For some, just getting centered and relaxing is a wonderful accomplishment. Others may want to work on being aware of or focusing on the sensations of the body, while still others may be comfortable going through the entire process. Go at the pace that is right for you. Going too slowly may be agitating for some, and too quickly may not be enough for others. Try to strike a happy medium—sticking with it the best you can and just breathing if it becomes too much. This is something that is "practiced," which means it's done repeatedly over time. Just simply notice your experience. And the next time you do it, notice that experience. Every time will be different.

Step 1: Getting Centered

The first step is quieting the mind. As discussed before, the *signal breath* is an easy exercise with the following benefits: (1) it takes only a few seconds and (2) it physiologically reduces tension and increases relaxation. It goes like this: Take in a deep breath, inhaling through your nose. Hold it for several seconds (about 5 seconds depending on what is comfortable for you), and then slowly let it out through your mouth. Feel the relaxation. It works best to do two to three cycles to fully relax.

Feel yourself sitting in the chair, your feet on the floor and back in an upright position with your arms and hands resting comfortably in your lap. Allow yourself to sink into the chair, relaxing your body . . . and breathe.

Step 2: Focusing on Sensations in Your Body

The next step is focusing on or "tuning into" the sensations of the body. This can be accomplished through an exercise called the *body scan*.

Start with bringing your attention to your feet. Feel the soles of your feet touching your shoes and your shoes touching the floor. Notice how your feet feel. Are they warm/cold, heavy/light, tingly? Do you sense that there is tension in your feet? Now focus on your ankles. Take a moment to feel the sensations of your ankles. Now focus on your calves. How do they feel? Are you holding any tension there? Bring your focus to your knees, your kneecaps, and the area behind your knees where your leg bends. What do you notice? Next move to your thighs. Tune in. Do you feel any tension? And breathe. . . .

Now bring your focus to your lower back. . . then your mid-back . . . and your upper back. Feel your back. Is there any tension? Now bring your attention to your stomach area. What do you notice in this area of your body? What do you feel? Next, go to your lungs and upper chest. Any tension? Spend some time feeling your shoulders. Are you holding tension in your shoulders? Again, breathe. . . . Tune into your neck and all the muscles connecting your shoulders through your neck and up to your head. What do you notice here? Now focus on your jaw—wiggle your jaw and see if this area is tight or relaxed. Bring your focus to your face, your forehead . . . eyes . . . eyebrows . . . cheeks . . . and mouth. Do you notice any tension? Breathe . . . and just notice the sensations in your body.

Step 3: Identifying the Feelings

The third step is decoding the messages in your body. Following the *body scan* is an exercise called the *emotional scan*. Again, start with your feet and quickly scan your body, putting an imaginary red X on the parts that are still tense. Then go back and find each red X and ask yourself, "What am I feeling here?" Take some time to "tune in" or pay attention to your feelings. If you can't get an answer, ask yourself, "Is it anger?" Then wait and listen. Your body will tell you if the word is accurate. Look for a sensation that feels like "Yes!" Go through the same procedure using the following words: hurt, fear, and sadness. Do any of these "ring true" or feel right to you? When you get an emotion for your first red X then proceed to Step 4. This part of the exercise is similar to Gendlin's focusing procedure (2007). When "focusing," continue to ask yourself what you are feeling until you hit the root or core of your feeling. Gendlin describes this as "feeling the body moving forward."

Step 4: Decoding the Message

Next ask yourself, "What is this feeling (or tension) communicating to me?" Maybe an image or a thought will come to you. Maybe the feeling is related to something that happened earlier in the day or maybe it is related to something that was unresolved from long ago. The body has its own ability to remember feelings. That is why sometimes people spontaneously recall emotional memories when they are having a body massage. Release the logical part of your brain and let yourself experience whatever comes up for you. Ask yourself, "Why am I feeling this way?" "What am I thinking?" See if you can identify the associated thoughts with your feelings. Are your thoughts really fears? Unresolved issues from the past? Or worries about what could happen in the future? When you get an answer then proceed to Step 5.

Step 5: Releasing the Feeling and the Tension

The final step is releasing the emotion, and thereby releasing the tension. Focus on the area in your body that is tense. Ask yourself, "Am I ready to release it and let it go?" If the answer is "No," then ask, "Is there something I still need to express or is there an action I need to do to help me feel complete with this issue?" Breathe into the tense area and notice what happens. Thank your body for providing the communication to you. Everyone appreciates a thank-you, including your body! It may sound silly, but thanking the body actually helps to release whatever is stored in the area of tension. Just simply say, "Thank you for communicating this message to me." Then move on to the next area of tension and repeat Steps 3 to 5 until you got all of your messages and your body is completely relaxed. End with two to three *cleansing breaths* (deep breath through the nose and out with a sigh).

If you need help in releasing emotion that is pent up in your body, you can write about it, talk to a friend or therapist about it, scream, cry, lift weights, punch a pillow, get a massage, or do whatever helps you to release the feeling (that is, of course, not harmful to yourself or anyone else). A good brisk walk is always a good option, as it gives you time to clear your head and releases mood enhancing endorphins—plus, you can feel good about doing something healthy!

Step 6: Deciding on Your Response

Now think about what have you learned by identifying your feelings and your thoughts. What are you responding to? Is there an unresolved issue, something that needs to be communicated or discussed, or an appropriate action that you would like to take? What will help you feel resolved about the situation? Remember to think through all the potential consequences and repercussions of your actions. Do they lead to an outcome that you desire?

Eventually, communicating with your body becomes easier. Your body will get your attention with an ache or pain. You can quickly tune in, get your message, thank your body for the communication, and then release it. Try it the next time you are unsure about a situation. What does your body communicate about how you feel?

The Box of Feelings

By the way, your box of feelings has not been forgotten! Instead of blasting open the box, we will slowly discover your feelings related to MST as we address one topic at a time in this class. For now, practice the *decoding your feelings* exercise to help you feel more comfortable and in control of experiencing feelings.

FEELINGS COME AND THEY GO

Feelings come and they go. They are impermanent, fleeting experiences.

Feelings are like waves. They build to a peak and then subside.

Feelings are like the weather—ever changing and never lasting.

Feelings are like the morning mist that dissolves with the rising sun.

Feelings are like lightning that quickly crackles across the sky.

Feelings are like a cloud gently floating by.

Feelings are like an old memory of something sweet long ago.

Feelings are like a bullet train speeding down the tracks.

Feelings are like cotton candy or a snowflake melting on your tongue.

Feelings are like a shy kitten darting from under a blanket.

Feelings are like a sailboat changing direction according to the wind.

Feelings come and they go. Feelings come and they go.

CHAPTER 2 SUMMARY POINTS

- What are feelings? Feelings are information; they are the body's way of expressing vital information about a situation.

- What happens if you avoid feelings? How can this be detrimental to your life?

- Feelings come from our thoughts. What information do feelings tell us? Anger is usually an indicator that something is wrong. Fear is usually an indicator that something is dangerous. Sadness is usually an indicator of a loss. Joy is an indicator of happiness.

- Feelings are physical sensations For example, anger may be experienced as tension in the jaw, shoulders, and arms as well as increased temperature and heart rate. Feelings come and they go— *they are meant to flow through us like water flows through a garden hose.* They may be intense, but they will pass.

- Feelings are responses, not facts. They are responses to how you think about a situation, but just because you have a strong feeling doesn't make the reason for the feeling true.

- Feelings are part of neural networks in the brain. There is nothing more convincing than an emotional experience to reinforce or strengthen the bond between a certain thought and a feeling. You can change the network of associated thoughts, feelings, and behaviors by changing any part of the system that leads to *new experiences.*

- *Decoding your feelings* is a six-step exercise to understand feelings through awareness of sensation in the body, including (1) Getting centered, (2) Focusing on sensations, (3) Identifying the feelings, (4) Decoding the message, (5) Releasing the feeling and tension, and (6) Deciding on a response.

Nightmares and Getting a Good Night's Sleep

3

Sleep hath its own world, and a wide realm of wild reality. And dreams in their development have breath, and tears, and tortures, and the touch of joy.

—*Lord Byron*

■ *Opening exercises: Building trust*
(Day 1: Follow the hand, Day 2: Mirrors)
■ *Closing exercises: Aromatherapy*
(Day 1: Explore different scents, Day 2: Make nightmare sachets)

SLEEP AND NIGHTMARES

Have you ever had trouble falling asleep—or been frightened by a scary dream? If the answer is yes, you are not alone. Sleep problems are among the most common symptoms associated with trauma. People who have experienced a traumatic event often have trouble falling and staying asleep. They may have certain dreams that recur regularly for years or resurface after long periods of time. And rather than simple bad dreams, they may be so scary that the dread of experiencing them makes falling asleep difficult. No matter how they occur, insomnia, fitful sleep, and nightmares may get in the way of getting needed rest.

Sleep is essential for restoring the mind and body and it has a strong impact on emotional, mental, and physical well-being. Sleep can help relieve stress, aid in problem solving, and help in healing and strengthening the immune system. For survivors of trauma, sleep is not just about being unable to fall and/or stay asleep at night; it also frequently involves a variety of concerns such as the fear of being vulnerable or out of control, worries about being unsafe such as the possibility of someone breaking and entering and/or being attacked by an intruder, and the unpleasant anticipation of having nightmares. In this chapter, we will discuss strategies for good sleep, including the following elements: (1) Good sleep habits, (2) Insomnia, (3) Presleep routine, (4) Immediate nightmare remedies, and (5) Understanding and rescripting nightmares.

GOOD SLEEP HABITS

A good night's sleep begins during the day! There are several things that you can do that either sets you up for a good or poor night of sleep. To start, it is important to avoid caffeine or other stimulants within several hours of sleep. A good rule of thumb is to avoid caffeine—which can be found in chocolate and other foods as well as in coffee, tea, and soda—within 6 hours of bedtime. It is also helpful to avoid taking naps during the day, or exercising within 2 hours of bedtime. Engaging in relaxing activities such as meditation or prayer, taking a warm bath, listening to soft music, or reading something positive and enjoyable may be helpful. Additionally, some sleep experts advise not using the bed for activities other than for sleep (or sexual activity). Good sleep habits help everyone get better sleep, regardless of specific issues.

INSOMNIA

Insomnia is a specific condition that describes when someone has difficulty falling or staying asleep. It could include *initial insomnia*, which is difficulty falling asleep; difficulty staying asleep (frequently waking up and not being able to get back to sleep); or *early morning awakening*, which is waking up too early and not being able to get back to sleep—all of which may leave you feeling tired the next day instead of feeling rested. *Primary insomnia* occurs when a person is having sleep problems that are not directly associated with any other health condition, while *secondary insomnia* is related to a health condition that interferes with your sleep, such as pain. Insomnia is considered chronic when someone has had these difficulties at least 3 nights a week and lasting for at least 1 month. There are several treatments for insomnia, including good sleep habits, stimulus control therapy, and sleep restriction therapy.

Stimulus control therapy is designed to help condition the mind and body to sleep. This includes setting a consistent time to go to bed and to wake up. It also means not using the bed for any other activities except sleep (and sex). If you can't fall asleep within 30 minutes, instead of tossing and turning, it's advised to get up, do something relaxing or boring, and return when you are sleepy. Also, it means no daytime naps. If you are trying to reset your sleep routine, it's important not to nap because then you won't be tired when it's time for bed. If you absolutely must nap, then it should be short. Anything over 20 minutes will disrupt your sleep and actually make you feel more tired and groggy.

Sleep restriction is a technique to address the frustration of lying in bed and not sleeping. Instead of not sleeping, you would be instructed to wait to go to bed for a couple of hours until you are tired, but to still get up at the same time. This decreases the time spent in bed, causing partial sleep deprivation. It should help make you more tired the next night. Once your sleep has improved, your time in bed can be gradually increased back to your regular bedtime.

Did You Know . . .

The number one saboteur of good sleep is the fear of not being able to sleep. The fear of not sleeping mobilizes the stress response and will certainly keep you awake! Another saboteur is worry. Worrying about what has happened, what could happen, and anything else on your mind will also interfere with sleep. One strategy is to have a worry journal by your bed. Write down everything on your mind and know it will be there when you wake up! This will help keep you from reviewing your worries while you're in bed instead of sleeping.

Good Sleep Habits for Restful Sleep

DOs	DON'Ts
Take a warm bath or shower before bed (maybe use a nice bodywash that smells good to you)	Go to sleep with unresolved arguments (try to work them out or write your thoughts down so you are not ruminating about them)
Drink chamomile or another relaxing, noncaffeinated herbal tea (a warm beverage can be very relaxing)	Drink caffeine within 6 hours of bedtime (caffeine does impair sleep!)
Massage hands and feet with lotion (this is relaxing and easy to do)	Eat a large meal or spicy foods (this can also contribute to restlessness or bad dreams)
Read inspirational works (the purpose of this is to have positive thoughts before sleep)	Read a scary book (this will increase the chance of having a bad dream)
Stretch and relax the body (light stretches can reduce tension)	Exercise vigorously within 2 hours before bed (this will keep you awake)
Breathe deeply (imagine breathing in, filling your entire body with air, and then exhaling completely all the way from your toes)	Worry about things you cannot change (Worry is a great way to disrupt sleep! Write down your thoughts to keep you from ruminating)
Listen to relaxing music (instrumental music but not something that will "stick" in your head) or do a boring task to make you sleepy	Watch the news or a TV drama within 2 hours of bedtime (this is stimulating and can disrupt sleep)
Prepare a comfortable sleep space for yourself (e.g., a cool, quiet, dark room; clean sheets; clean pajamas; and a decluttered area)	Spend time in bed not sleeping (if after 30 minutes you are not sleeping, DO get up and do something relaxing or really boring, such as reading a textbook or counting)
Wake up at the same time every morning to set your sleep cycles	Stay in bed after your wake-up time, snooze past your alarm time, or take long naps (more than 20 min)—these have been found to make people feel more tired and groggy

What behaviors can you do to enhance your sleep?

_____

_____

_____

_____

_____

_____

_____

_____

_____

Did You Know . . .

Sleep occurs in cycles lasting 90 to 120 minutes, and we experience many of these cycles each night. Each of these cycles is made up of four stages. The first two stages are nonrapid eye movement (NREM) sleep. In the first stage, we begin to go from a state of being awake to light sleeping; during this phase, it is common to experience a sense of falling. As we progress into the second stage, temperature drops and heart rate slows; at this stage, the body regenerates tissues, bones, and muscle. In the third phase, we begin to enter deep sleep, characterized by rapid eye movement (REM). The next, or fourth, phase is the deepest REM sleep, and it is when the most intense dreaming occurs.

PRESLEEP ROUTINE

A presleep routine is a specific set of behaviors that you do every night that cues your body that it is time to relax and go to sleep. For example, children benefit from a routine such as "take a bath, put on pajamas, brush your teeth, get into bed, read a story, sing a goodnight song, and end with a kiss on the forehead while saying goodnight." This elaborate routine, if done consistently, trains the mind and body to go to sleep. Similarly, adults can also benefit from a routine. Your routine may consist of "take a shower, write in your journal, listen to soothing music, relax or meditate, and set a good intention for a safe and sound sleep." This can also include a safety check of your home, such as making sure doors and windows are locked. If you do your routine consistently, you will get the best results.

Setting a Good Intention

Part of your presleep routine could include setting a positive intention to have a safe and restful night. This could include positive self-talk that focuses on the fact that you are ready—physically as well as mentally—to have a safe and peaceful sleep. "My house is secure and I feel safe," or "I am relaxed, calm, and ready to rest now," are two examples. Writing these messages on cards and reading them before sleep may be useful.

What is a positive message that you can tell yourself to set a good intention for sleep?

_____

_____

Engaging Your Senses

Another aspect of your presleep routine could be engaging your senses for a positive and relaxed experience. For example, smelling a pleasant aroma; having a cool sip of water; using a soft, comforting blanket; wearing clean pajamas; and sleeping on clean, fresh sheets can help you feel peaceful and calm. You can also look at beautiful photos of places or things—possibly from nature—to help you focus your imagery. You can also read something that makes you feel comforted or inspired.

Creating an Invisible Negativity Shield

Imagery can be a powerful tool to induce feelings of safety. For example, this can be achieved by imagining a guardian angel watching over you or having a force field of protection around you. You can construct an image such as: "Imagine that your home is protected by an invisible negativity shield. This shield is constructed out of a golden light that resonates at such a high vibration that no one can see it. Now, imagine this light is swirling around your home, surrounding it, and creating a force field that is so powerful that it wards off any and all negativity. Anyone or anything that would try to get near your home without your permission would be repelled and bounce off the light." You can put up this force field of light by intending that it be there. Imagine it and then visualize it. You can use this one or create your own imagery of safety and protection (Katz, 2005).

What will be your presleep routine?

_____

_____

> ### *Did You Know . . .*
>
> Some eye movements during REM sleep—the time during the sleep cycle when you are most likely to dream—correspond to specific movements in dreams. Some researchers believe that this may mean that we "watch" dreams in the same way that we watch television, films, or computer monitors.

WHAT IS A NIGHTMARE?

A nightmare is a dream that wakes you up from your sleep, usually with disturbing or scary content. Whether or not you remember the dream, nightmares can provoke intense feelings of fear and panic and disrupt your sleep. It is not uncommon to experience a type of anxiety response similar to what was experienced during an actual trauma. Whether the nightmare is based on actual events and images you have seen or is a symbolic representation of emotions that you have experienced, nightmares can seem terrifyingly real—and disrupt your sleep!

While scary dreams are not "real," it is important to recognize that your feelings of terror are authentic. You may be subconsciously "triggered" to have a nightmare by many things, such as an anniversary of an event or being exposed to something reminiscent of the trauma, which can be anything from certain music to something seen on TV, or even a particular type of weather. Considering the emotions that are being replayed through dream images is key to understanding and treating nightmares.

Nightmare Remedies

Working on coping with nightmares begins with the "good sleep habits" that were discussed earlier. It is important to be active in creating a positive sleep environment, developing and implementing a plan of action if you have a nightmare, and working on understanding and rescripting the dreams to eventually stop having the nightmares.

When people have nightmares, they may wake up feeling frightened, angry, disoriented, and breathless. It may be impossible to go back to sleep—many people report spending the rest of the night fighting off feelings of terror. Even worse, if you do go back to sleep, you may resume the nightmare as if continuing the bad movie in your mind. The immediate concern is to return to a feeling of safety—and use strategies to return to sleep peacefully.

To do this, it is important to remind yourself that you are in "the here and now" and wake up fully after you have a nightmare. In order to *not* return to the dream, it is very important to be completely awake, aware, and grounded after a nightmare. To this end, it helps to actually get out of bed, stand up, and feel your feet on the floor. It is also helpful to engage your senses after you wake from a nightmare. Taking deep breaths and sipping water or splashing cool water on your face can help. Because the sense of smell is a powerful trigger (for both good and bad memories), smelling something good can give you an instantaneous positive feeling and help you feel grounded, present, and relaxed.

Next, it is important to feel safe in your current environment. It can be helpful to have some comforting objects on the nightstand, such as a crystal, a religious object, photographs of beautiful places or people you love, and so on, and take a moment to pick up these objects. You may also get comfort from pets, doing a safety check of the house, or taking a few *cleansing breaths* to reduce tension.

Finally, it is a good idea to "plant" positive feelings through self-talk and visualization. Some positive messages might include: "I'm okay," "I can handle this," "I'm safe," "I release my fear and feel calm," or any other message that is simple and comforting. Imagining your "negativity shield" or a beautiful scene from nature, remembering and visualizing specific good times, or reading an inspirational passage can also help.

If you are having difficulty becoming sleepy again, you can do a boring task such as counting or reading a manual or phone book or something that is not interesting for you. Each time you succeed at dispelling your fears and reclaiming your sleep, it builds resilience and paves the way for continued success!

THE RATIONAL AND EXPERIENTIAL SYSTEMS

To better understand dreams, it helps to understand how the brain processes information. According to psychologist Seymour Epstein, we have two systems for processing information: the *experiential* and the *rational* systems. The experiential system (e.g., based on experiencing sensations) is our system for processing emotions and imagery. The rational system is for processing facts, theories, and abstract thoughts. It is logical, analytical, and typically what we think of as "intelligence." However, Epstein found that intelligent people do not necessarily lead healthier, happier, and more productive lives. In fact, his research found that IQ was the only measure that did not correlate with measures of success in living! Instead, it was a measure of the experiential mind or the emotional side of the brain that best predicted success in living. This part of the brain is a strong guiding force that influences every aspect of our lives, including our ability to cope with stress and our physical health.

Imagine someone trying to change your mind about which car to buy. You have your heart set on one car, but your friend tells you another car is safer, has better gas mileage, and is considerably less expensive. Which one are you going to choose? Your rational mind may consider the facts while your experiential mind considers how you will *feel* in your new car. This is an example of when the two systems may be in conflict with each other. Epstein's research further describes how most people tend to think we make decisions with our rational mind, but when it comes down to the actual decision, the experiential mind often times wins out.

For example, in a series of studies examining choice, participants were able to state that there is no difference in the probability of choosing a red jelly bean in a jar where there is one red jelly bean and nine white ones, or in a jar where there are ten red jelly beans and ninety white ones. Participants reported that both jars had the same chance—1 in 10—of pulling a red jelly bean. However, when given a chance to win a cash prize, guess which jar most participants chose—the one with 10 red jelly beans! When asked why, participants stated they felt they had a better chance of winning (in spite of previously reporting that the probabilities are exactly the same)!

To further illustrate this, Epstein and his colleagues repeated the experiment, but this time only put nine red jelly beans in the second jar. Now there was actually a lower probability of choosing a red bean from this jar. Which jar do you think people chose for the chance to win a cash prize? If you guessed the one with nine red beans, you are right! This same result was even found with eight red jelly beans! Only when the jar was down to seven red jelly beans was the pattern broken. But this is a powerful demonstration of the influence of the experiential or emotional mind when it comes to making decisions.

Have you ever said to yourself, "I know I should _____ (break up with my boyfriend, change jobs, confront my mother, stop this addictive behavior, go to the gym, etc.), but I just can't"? The rational mind knows you are not in a good situation and you rationally "should" make a change, but you don't. Why not? Something else is guiding your decisions—your experiential mind! The experiential mind may be responding to an uncomfortable or painful experience from the past or may be anticipating an uncomfortable or painful experience in the future. Why would you want to change if you are anticipating being in some form of pain? It is the experiential system that blocks as well as supports behavior change.

RATIONAL SYSTEM	EXPERIENTIAL SYSTEM
Linear, sequential processing; $a + b = c$	Holistic processing/gut feelings
Analytical, abstract thoughts	Associations and emotions
Processes words and numbers	Processes metaphors, stories, imagery
Slow to process, quick to change	Quick to process, slow to change
Requires justification, logic, evidence	Self-evidently valid, knowing by experience

Dreams and nightmares reside in the experiential system. This is where you process your feelings—and like dreams, something in the current time may be associated with the past; it may be represented in your dreams as a metaphor or symbol. You may wake up feeling emotionally activated (e.g., scared, angry, upset, happy) because something of emotional significance is being processed in your experiential mind.

Example of a Symbolic Representation in a Dream

One of my clients reported in session that she had a vivid dream of cats wandering throughout her house. Her doors and windows were open, and there were cats in all of the rooms. They were just wandering around. She did not report feeling afraid, angry, or hurt. She said she knew she was safe and the cats were nice, but she did feel "exposed" because "cats were in her house." When she said it out loud we both laughed, as we realized that "cats" represented "Dr. Katz" and she was feeling exposed in psychotherapy. Sometimes dreams are a concrete way to express thoughts and feelings.

Another interesting quality of the experiential system is that it does not process time in a linear fashion like the rational system. Memories about something that happened 3 months or 10 years ago are experienced the same when you recall them, and you feel the sensations as if it were happening right now. Because the experiential system has no concept of time, memories can be recalled and experienced as if they were really happening. Similarly, a nightmare can be experienced as if it was an actual experience and you may wake up feeling as if you were experiencing trauma (e.g., heart racing, sweating, feeling afraid, etc.). The experiential system does not know the difference. In this way, using the rational system can help process or move information out of the experiential system into the rational system, giving it time and place. This will help process the images and emotions that are causing nightmares.

The experiential mind also does not know the difference between imagined experience and real experience. Your body will respond to images just like it does to experience. To test this idea, try the following imagery exercise about a lemon.

THE LEMON EXERCISE

(Note: This works best if the facilitator reads the imagery while participants close their eyes.) Start with a *signal breath* (deep breath in, hold it at the top, and then exhale). Imagine going into your kitchen and opening the refrigerator door. Inside you see a bright yellow lemon. As you pick up the lemon you can feel it is cool in your hand. Put the lemon on the counter and take a knife and slice it in half. A spray of juice squirts onto the counter and you can smell the fresh citrus scent in the air. As you separate the halves, you can see the light glistening on the pulp. Now take one of the lemon halves and slice it again so that you have two quarter wedges. Lift one of the wedges to your mouth . . . and bite into the lemon. *(Wait for a few moments to allow people to feel the sensations.)* Now open your eyes.

Did you notice the saliva pooling in your mouth? Your body had a physiological reaction—but to what? Was there really a lemon or only an image of a lemon? Your body responded as if there was a real lemon because your body responds to the images and thoughts you generate.

UNDERSTANDING NIGHTMARES

As with memories of trauma, during nightmares you may feel as if you are either in the middle of an event that occurred years ago or in a new fearful event created by your imagination. While nightmares can be extremely unpleasant, they can also be useful as a door into your unconscious mind, offering clues about the things that may be bothering you.

Dreams are the natural way for the unconscious (experiential) mind to express itself and attempt to resolve blocked or poorly processed emotional issues. When you have experienced trauma, you may have significant feelings that were never processed. Working with a therapist or on your own, it may help to consider and write down the content or story of the dream; the feelings that you experienced during the dream; and the memories, thoughts, or images associated with those feelings. In other words, what unresolved emotion is the nightmare bringing up? Tracking the emotions, metaphors, stories, and symbols—all components of the experiential system—may help unlock the mystery of interpreting dreams.

Keep a Dream Journal!

Keeping track of your dreams and their associated feelings can help you understand possible patterns in your nightmares. After a dream, jot down the images and events that you remember and how you felt in the dream. Just write enough so that you will remember the images in the morning so this doesn't keep you awake all night! In the morning, you can write more details. Use the following worksheet to analyze the dream.

DREAM JOURNAL

What were you feeling when you woke up from the dream?

_____

_____

What were you dreaming about? (What was happening?) What images do you remember? (Write anything you remember, even strange things.)

_____

_____

_____

_____

_____

The next morning you can think about the dream. Do any of the images remind you of something from the past? What associations do you have with the images? Is anything symbolic or representative of something important to you?

_____

_____

_____

_____

RESCRIPTING A DREAM

It's your dream, and it is possible for you to alter it by consciously rewriting, or "rescripting," a different ending. First, select a dream that you would like to change. Now, think of a positive or satisfying resolution to the dream. Make up anything you like—it can be fantasy or something more "real." The point is to come up with something that leaves you feeling satisfied and confident, instead of how you felt during or after the dream you wanted to change. This is not something to do while you are lying down, ready to go to sleep. Instead it is something you want to work on while you are awake. For example, let's say you are being chased in your dream and wake up with a racing heartbeat, sweating, and feeling afraid. How might you want to rescript this? Maybe you imagine yourself turning around and confronting the person chasing you. Imagine saying "No!" while you grow large and the chaser gets smaller. Maybe the chaser is startled and runs away from you! How would you feel? (Remember the lemon exercise? When you imagine something, your body will feel it.)

Once you rescript the ending of your dream, practice it using your imagination. To practice your new dream, sit in a comfortable position and relax your body and mind for a few minutes with stretches, breathing (e.g., *signal breath*), or any other method that might be helpful. Once you feel calm and quiet, visualize your dream, running through it as though you were watching a video. When you come to a point that is unpleasant, replace the old part with the new one you created. Imagine it as vividly as you can, "making it up" as you go if necessary. Make a special point to experience and let your body feel the new sense of confidence, freedom, and empowerment from your new ending. You can make it realistic or you can use fantasy—you can be a superhero, or you can imagine someone coming to help you such as a friend, ally, or an angel … there is no limit to your power here! Practice your new dream over the course of several days to gain mastery.

Finally, give yourself the clear message that not only are these new thought patterns in your waking life, but that tonight—or whenever you have this dream—it will include the new, more fulfilling, and positive part that you have created. You may even tell yourself that you will be able to recognize the dream as a dream while it is happening, in which case you can consciously direct it toward a satisfying outcome. This is also called lucid dreaming.

Is there a recurring dream or an image in your mind that you would like to rescript? If so, what is it and how would you like to change the ending? Then practice or "rehearse" your dream with the new ending. You can practice this daily for several days until you feel confident in your ability to change your dream.

MY SLEEP ROUTINE

1. **What daytime activities can you increase or decrease to enhance good sleep?**

_____

_____

_____

_____

2. **What will be your presleep routine to prepare you for sleep?** (e.g., "Take a shower, meditate for 10 minutes, read a passage from an inspirational book, think of a positive image to dream about. Then when I am in bed, I will put up my invisible negativity shield, and set my intention to be safe and relaxed for a good night's sleep!")

_____

_____

_____

_____

3. **What will you do if you have a nightmare?** (e.g., "Wake up, smell something nice, put my feet on the ground, wash my face, tell myself I am okay, change my imagery to something positive, and write a few notes in my dream journal.")

_____

_____

_____

_____

4. **What will you do to process your nightmare the next day?** (e.g., "Write about it, talk to a therapist, think about the emotional theme, and explore associations and triggers.")

_____

_____

_____

_____

THE POWER OF SMELL

As a scent enters the nose, it travels through the cranial nerve and the olfactory bulb. The olfactory bulb is part of the limbic system, where emotions are processed in the brain. The limbic system is also where the amygdala resides, which plays a role in emotional memories. (More about this will be discussed in the following chapters.) The olfactory system also relates to the part of the brain called the hippocampus, which is critical in developing memories. Because the olfactory bulb can influence both the amygdala and the hippocampus, smell can have a powerful effect on either recalling or stopping an emotional memory. Unlike other senses that are processed through the frontal lobe or the thinking part of the brain, smell is the only sense that bypasses this part and can induce a direct and immediate emotional experience. This is particularly helpful after a nightmare or while you are being triggered. Your mind may not be able to focus or think . . . but you can smell!

What memories do you recall when you smell apple cinnamon, pumpkin spice, vanilla, or lavender? Even if you don't have a specific memory, these scents may be pleasant and could enhance your mood. In other words, these smells can make you feel good!

NIGHTMARE SACHETS

When you wake up from a nightmare, an effective strategy to counteract it is to smell something good. This will go directly to the emotional center of your brain. This is particularly helpful because you may be actively thinking about negative or scary things and may not be able to shift your thinking very quickly. But a smell works instantly, regardless of what you are thinking about. Keep something that smells good by your bed, such as a sachet, scented candle, or piece of wonderful-smelling soap. When you wake up, take a deep sniff of the good smell and it will help you feel better . . . fast.

How to Make a Bedside Sachet

Cut a 6-inch square out of a breathable material (e.g., not plastic or vinyl). Place a cotton ball in the middle and crush some potpourri, cloves, dried flowers, shaved soap, or anything else that smells good to you. Avoid putting aromatherapy oils in the cloth, as it will eventually leak and become rancid. Gather up the ends, making a little pouch. Use ribbon to tie the pouch together. You can curl the ribbon for a decorative touch. Some group members like to make two, one for their bedside and one to carry with them, as this is also effective for triggers and anxiety.

CHAPTER 3 SUMMARY POINTS

- *Practice good sleep habits.* Avoid caffeine or other stimulants within several hours of sleep. Avoid taking naps during the day or exercising within 2 hours of bedtime. Relax prior to sleeping by taking a warm bath, listening to soft music, or reading something enjoyable.

- *Insomnia.* Insomnia can be addressed by good sleep habits, stimulus control (only use the bed for sleep and wake up at the same time), and sleep restriction (set bedtime later than usual but still get up at the same time, which should enhance feeling sleepy the next night).

- *Develop a presleep routine.* This is a specific set of behaviors that you do every night to cue your body that it is time to relax and go to sleep.

- *Postnightmare remedies.* Wake up after a nightmare by getting out of bed, standing up and feeling your feet on the floor, taking deep breaths, sipping some water, or splashing water on your face. Smell something good to help you wake up and instill positive feelings. Wake up enough to interrupt the nightmare but then relax to return to a restful calm state before returning to sleep. Engaging in a boring task can also cause you to become sleepy and help you return to sleep.

- *Experiential and rational systems.* We have two systems for processing information: the *experiential* and the *rational* systems. The experiential system processes emotions and imagery. The rational system processes facts, theories, and abstract thoughts. Dreams occur in the experiential system. The body responds to the imagery of a nightmare as if it is a real experience.

- *Understanding and rescripting nightmares.* Dreams may be a natural way for the unconscious (experiential) mind to express itself and attempt to resolve blocked or poorly processed emotional issues. You can rescript your dream by consciously rewriting a different ending and then rehearsing the new ending using imagery.

Triggers and Anxiety

4

Health is a state of complete physical, mental and social well-being, and not merely the absence of disease or infirmity.
—*World Health Organization, 1948*

- *Opening exercises: Building group cohesion*
  (Day 1: Pass the object, Day 2: Group mirror)
- *Closing exercises: Guided imagery*
  (Day 1: Tropical beach scene, Day 2: Mountain waterfall)

TRIGGERING ANXIETY

Whether it's mild worry or an all-out panic attack, anxiety is one of the most common feelings for people who have experienced trauma. And while anxiety may take many different forms, its impact is the same. Anxiety imposes itself on people and robs them of the ability to take pleasure in things. It intrudes on time and energy, and it may even invade people's lives to the point that it is hard to get through the day. This chapter will explore some ways to tackle anxiety and its triggers.

What are "triggers" of anxiety? A trigger can be anything that serves as a reminder of a past trauma such as a sight, sound, smell, taste, feeling, or object. This is how it works: Let's say you are going about your day and you smell a certain type of cologne and all of a sudden your heart starts to race, and you feel anxious and unsafe. You may or may not even be aware that what you smelled was a "trigger." The trigger reminded you of a past trauma. In this example, someone was wearing that cologne when the traumatic event occurred. Because of its association or connection to trauma, smelling the cologne takes on meaning and may serve to trigger an anxiety response, like flipping a switch in the brain. The experience of smelling the cologne then sets off a chain of neurochemical reactions. These reactions may lead to physical as well as emotional responses, from feeling lightheaded or agitated to having sweaty palms or feeling unable to breathe. On the one hand, the body is having an adaptive response to the perception of danger—which is the "fight, flight, or freeze" response. However, there is no actual danger in the current situation, simply a memory of danger. But the body doesn't know the difference. It reacts as if there really is danger. This is because the emotional memory resides in the experiential system. And once the chemical reactions are activated, it can make the person experiencing it feel upset and worried because now they are having a sudden attack of anxiety. Thoughts of concern and worry only serve to prolong the anxiety and thereby delay the activation of the neurochemicals that tell the body to shut down the anxiety response (e.g., recover back to normal).

In addition, because the trigger often catches people off guard, it is the surprise element that makes it especially distressing. Though you might not have thought about an event for years, a particular trigger can make you feel as if you are somehow back in that situation. In fact, a trigger may provoke the strong feeling of re-experiencing the event—and being re-traumatized! Because triggers can be so disturbing, people may develop a terror of experiencing them. This terror can make people want to avoid going places or doing things, especially with other people, thus blocking freedom, spontaneous joy, and the ability to be in the present.

> The key to change . . . is to let go of fear.
> —Roseanne Cash

UNDERSTANDING TRIGGERS

Pavlov's Dogs

To understand triggers, it is helpful to review the experiment of a scientist named Ivan Pavlov. While working in his laboratory investigating the digestive system in dogs, he discovered a conditioned reaction in his dogs that we now call *classical conditioning*. He noticed that when he gave his dogs meat powder they would salivate because they loved the tasty treat. Then he started ringing a bell just before he gave them the meat powder. This is called "pairing": presenting something neutral with something that naturally produces a response. After several times, Pavlov noticed that when he rang the bell even without giving the dogs the meat powder, they would salivate. The bell became "conditioned" from something neutral to something that produced a response all on its own.

Meat → salivation

Neutral bell + meat → salivation

Bell alone → salivation

The bell has become conditioned to trigger salivation.

Trauma, by definition, is scary and dangerous. However, everything else that occurred at that time, which prior to the event was "neutral," has now been associated or paired with trauma. Those previous neutral sights, smells, sounds, tastes, and feelings are now triggers or reminders of trauma and can produce anxiety responses all on their own.

Threat of harm → anxiety

Neutral smells, sounds, and objects + threat of harm → anxiety

Smells, sounds, and objects → anxiety

Smells, sounds, and objects have become conditioned to trigger anxiety.

Pavlov also discovered that he could break the association between a neutral item and its provoking response, or "decondition the conditioned item," by ringing the bell several times without giving the dogs any meat powder. After a while the dogs learned that the bell was not going to get them any meat and they stopped salivating when they heard the bell. The bell was just a bell.

Likewise, there are treatments such as *exposure therapy* and *prolonged exposure* (Foa & Rothbaum, 1998) wherein neutral items are presented without a threat of harm and eventually those neutral items stop producing symptoms of anxiety.

There are several reasons why people may not naturally decondition triggers to anxiety if left on their own. One is that people tend to avoid things that they believe are scary, dangerous, and anxiety provoking. This limits opportunities to confront neutral items, and without any new experiences to disconfirm the belief that they are dangerous, the person remains afraid and continues to avoid these things, at all costs! (Remember the story of Mary avoiding parties in Chapter 2?)

Another problem is that people tend to partially re-experience flashes of trauma through nightmares, unresolved triggers, and repeated experiences of trauma. These reinforce or strengthen the associations or neural networks. So instead of deconditioning the associations, they become stronger!

A third problem is related to neurological changes that occur as a result of trauma. As an adaptive response to potential danger, the brain forms a web of connected neurons, or a neural network, that helps people recognize potential danger more quickly and efficiently. Therefore, it makes sense that people respond to triggers; the brain has marked these items as potentially dangerous and alerts the person to quickly mobilize into action. Every time something sets off the network, the associations are strengthened, making the network stronger and more efficient. After many years, it wouldn't take much to light up the network. Thus, it usually takes some conscious effort to weaken the trauma-related neural networks. It also takes effort to form new networks that are associated with reassurance, safety, relaxation, and trust.

NORMAL REACTIONS TO STRESS

To better understand traumatic stress, it is first important to understand people's natural response to stress. When people experience stress, the body mobilizes its resources to be able to handle the situation. With a perception of threat, the part of the brain called the amygdala sounds an alarm to alert the hypothalamus. This signals the activation of the adrenal glands to secrete neurotransmitters: epinephrine and norepinephrine. These neurotransmitters tell the body to get pumped up and ready to fight or run. It stimulates increased respiration, blood flow to the muscles, and increased energy. This is called the *fight or flight* response. This is a normal and adaptive response to stress to increase survival in the presence of danger. In other words, when you perceive danger or threat, your body reacts in a way that is designed to help you get out of the situation (fight or run). This may be experienced as anxiety, nervousness, agitation, muscle tension, flushing, and shallow breathing.

Two other common reactions to stress are the *dissociative freeze* response and the *tend and befriend* response. The *dissociative freeze* response, seen in both animals and humans, occurs in the face of an inescapable danger: an individual literally freezes in the hopes that the danger will not escalate and will soon pass. Many people are not aware that the freeze response is a normal and adaptive response to stress. People who have had sexual trauma may likely have had this response. Some people report that they literally couldn't move and couldn't scream for help. This is not their fault because their stress hormones made them frozen. It is possible that if they were able to fight or scream they may have gotten away, but more likely the perpetrator would have become more violent. In many cases, freezing during sexual trauma might have saved a person's life. Freezing is a normal and adaptive response.

The *tend and befriend* response seems specific to women, whereby in the face of uncertainty and danger women will seek each other and provide comfort to lessen the anxiety. Researcher Shelly Taylor found that the release of the hormone oxytocin may be responsible for this reaction (Taylor et al., 2000). More research is needed to fully understand this stress response.

How do you typically respond to stress (fight, flight, freeze, or tend and befriend)?

_____

_____

_____

When it is determined that there is no longer a threat, the brain signals the pituitary gland to release adrenocortiotropic hormone (ACTH) to activate the adrenal glands—to release hydrocortisone, cortisol. The cortisol will stop the alarm reaction and help restore the body to homeostasis, or back to the normal prestress level of functioning. This system is called the hypothalamic–pituitary–adrenal (HPA) axis. It regulates activation and inhibition of stress responses. This system helps you ramp up for protection and calm down when it is safe. It is normal and adaptive to have stress and your HPA axis helps you manage it.

An easy way to explain this is to imagine a stable filled with wild horses. These horses represent stress hormones. When an alarm of "danger" is sounded, the gates open and all of the horses run out, passing the message to other stables and activating wild horses throughout the brain. When a whistle is blown, this signals all the horses to go back into their stables. The HPA axis is the system that regulates the alarm, gates, horses, and whistle to return to the stables.

NORMAL VERSUS PTSD REACTIONS TO STRESS

People with PTSD may have problems with their HPA axis and have difficulty regulating their system. They may be more likely to perceive non-threatening things as extremely threatening. This causes increased stress responses (e.g., more frequent episodes of the horses running out of the stables). In addition, researchers such as Rachel Yehuda have found that those with PTSD have adrenal glands that do not produce enough cortisol (Yehuda et al., 2000). This means they cannot down-regulate, inhibit, or stop the stress response. In other words, the "whistle" that tells the horses to return to the stables doesn't work very well (i.e., the message is not strong enough), so it takes a long time for the horses to come back to the stables. This inability to calm down from stress combined with being more easily triggered by stress over time causes people to feel drained and exhausted—resulting in a general numbing.

In summary, the PTSD stress reaction is overwhelmed to the point of exhaustion—leading to numbing (i.e., not feeling anything)—but when something does trigger or activate the stress response, people with PTSD have a slower recovery and that, coupled with frequent triggering, leads to even more exhaustion.

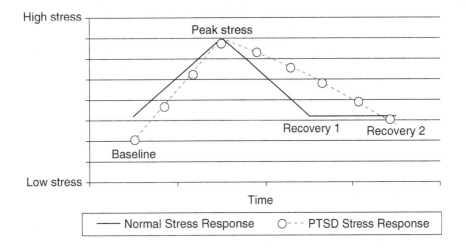

The dotted line shows that those with PTSD may have a numbing reaction and, therefore, a lower baseline than those without PTSD. Both groups have a similar stress reaction (peak response to the stress), but those with PTSD have a longer recovery time (i.e., it takes longer to come down).

HEALING TRIGGERS AND ANXIETY

The trick to healing triggers is to recognize what they actually are: sights, smells, and sounds that are reminders of trauma, *but are not actually dangerous.* Experiences come and go. The stress is a chemical response; it is temporary, fleeting, and will pass. Even if it takes a little while, knowing that it will pass— and it always does—can help you through it. Using the suggested techniques will help decrease the frequency (how often you have them), amplitude (level of distress it causes), and duration (how long it lasts). Observe the anxiety and wait for it to pass, like water passing through a garden hose. If you let the water flow, it goes out quickly and effortlessly. However, as discussed in the previous chapter, if you try to stop the water and kink the hose, it builds up pressure and discomfort. Anxiety passes quickest when you just let it flow through you without trying to change, stop, fix, or resist the experience.

Feelings come and they go . . . they are meant to pass through us like water passes through a garden hose.

COPE-ing With Anxiety Caused by Triggers

Learning specific skills to use when you experience triggers can help build self-confidence and reduce the fear of reacting to an intrusive thought or trigger in the future. One strategy is called "COPE" (Katz, 2005). C stands for *cleansing breath*, O stands for *observation*, P stands for *positive self-talk*, and E stands for *explanation.*

In this strategy, the *cleansing breath* signals your body to calm itself. This helps to reabsorb the stress hormones and reduce the anxiety. The *cleansing breath* helps signal to the body that it is time for all the horses to come back to the stables. It may take a minute, but the wild horses will come back!

Using the rational part of your mind, take a mental step back from the experience of anxiety by observing your situation and reactions. This can lessen the panicked feelings as well as help you gain important knowledge about what it was and why it triggered you. Next, coach yourself with positive self-talk through the anxiety. Finally, it is reassuring to tell yourself that what you just experienced was a trigger or anxiety.

Cleansing Breath

A *cleansing breath* is an inhale through the mouth and exhale with a sigh. Because people who are anxious tend to hold their breath, it is useful to particularly work on fully exhaling the breath, thereby releasing tension and facilitating breathing.

Observation

There are two things to observe. First, observe the environment to reassure yourself that there is no actual danger in the present moment. Next, observe the fight, flight, and freeze reaction of anxiety that is occurring in your body. Recognize that you are having normal symptoms of anxiety such as increased heart rate, sweating, light-headedness, and tight muscles.

Positive Self-Talk

Tell yourself positive and comforting statements. Reassure yourself that you're okay, this will pass, breathe, you're safe, and so on.

What can you say to yourself that will make you feel better when this happens?

_____

_____

Explanation

Remind yourself that this is only a trigger (not actual danger). This is only a temporary sensation of anxiety. Having a label to understand what is going on will lessen the intensity of the experience. Imagine telling yourself statements such as "What is happening to me?! Oh no, I might be having a heart attack! I could die! Everyone is staring at me!!" These are typical thoughts that people have when they are triggered. However, notice how much calmer you would feel if you told yourself something like this: "I'm okay, I know what this is. . . . It's a trigger of anxiety and it will pass in a couple of minutes. I'm having a normal fight or flight response, but because there is no danger, it is safe to calm down. I'm going to just watch myself have this experience and know it will pass as I continue to take slow, deep breaths, exhaling completely. . . ."

You can use the COPE technique several times until the anxiety passes. It may be useful to think about the image of water flowing through a hose . . . watching the feelings peak and subside . . . and the feelings will eventually pass, as they always do.

> **Cleansing breath:** Take several slow, deep breaths, exhaling completely.
>
> **Observation:** Realize you are not in danger and watch the anxious sensations and thoughts come and go.
>
> **Positive self-talk:** "I'm okay, and this will pass."
>
> **Explanation:** "This is an intrusive thought. This is just a normal response to a trigger."

> ### Did You Know . . .
>
> It can be helpful to write positive self-talk statements when you are *not* feeling anxious, such as: "I am strong and safe," "My feelings come and go, and soon I will feel better," and "I'm okay, this will pass," as well as positive messages that are more specific to you. Carry the notes with you and read them if you feel anxious.

When you're feeling anxious, remember that you're still you. You are not anxiety. Whenever you feel otherwise, remember that's just the anxiety talking. You are still you and hold the power in every moment.
—Deanne Repich

The Gift of Triggers

While triggers are disturbing and uncomfortable, they can also be useful. Though difficult to experience, triggers and intrusive thoughts also offer clues into our subconscious minds about experiences of trauma, providing important insight into why you may feel the way you do. Why do certain triggers carry such powerful meaning? Becoming aware of how and why you may be triggered may help you get to the root of the trauma, and help you understand the connections between your thoughts, feelings, and behaviors. They may help you come to terms with your past. And ultimately, they may help you heal.

For example, Eric was experiencing increased intrusive thoughts, which were causing him to feel a lot of anxiety. When this first started to happen, he was not consciously aware that it was the month of the third anniversary after the traumatic incident that he survived. When he made this connection and realized that the date was a trigger for him, it helped him explain the sudden increase of unpleasant symptoms. It also allowed him to confront more directly his feelings about the trauma, including bouts of fear, anger, and grief. Through experiencing and analyzing the meaning of this trigger, he began to feel less anxiety.

It makes perfect sense that you have anxiety responses when you are triggered, according to your experiential system. The neural networks associated with the trauma light up and mobilize you to react. However, even if your rational mind knows that the object is not dangerous, the experiential mind may still activate. For example, a woman who was raped in an elevator may rationally know that elevators are no more or less dangerous than before the trauma. However, every time she goes near an elevator she starts to panic and refuses to enter. Her past experience brings up emotional memories that are distinct from her rational thoughts. Nonetheless, she can utilize her rational mind to understand her reactions and coach herself to be open to new experiences. Then by having new safe and pleasant experiences on an elevator, she can weaken the association with fear and decrease her stress activation.

Panic Attacks

Panic attacks are a type of anxiety characterized by sudden overwhelming periods of anxiety with several physical symptoms, including shortness of breath, dizziness, and heart palpitations. This may or may not be brought on by a specific trigger or intrusive thought. Having a panic attack is extremely disturbing, and many people who experience them worry that they are having a heart attack—and fear they're going to die during the attack. Both having an anxiety attack and the anticipation of possibly having an attack in the future are extremely stressful.

How do you address these attacks? The first step in decreasing panic attacks is carefully identifying the specific symptoms that you experience. These are the "sensations" that are associated with the panic attack. These sensations may include intense feelings of fear, chest pain, heart palpitations, shortness of breath, dizziness, nausea, stomach upset, cold sweats, chills, hyperventilation, and trouble swallowing. Each of these feelings may be part of the body's natural response to anxiety, and may last for a few minutes or as long as half an hour—which can feel like forever! The COPE strategy can be used to manage panic attacks. COPE will decrease the length of the anxiety and may lessen the intensity of the experience. Find somewhere to sit, focus on breathing, and just allow the panic sensations to move through you like water passing through a hose. It will pass.

Phobias

Unlike panic attacks, which are usually associated with general anxiety, a phobia is an intense fear of a very specific item. In a panic attack, the trigger or source of the anxiety may or may not be consciously known; however, in a phobia, there is heightened awareness about the source of the anxiety and the person who has the phobia takes great lengths to avoid the specific fearful cause. Common phobias are fear of spiders, snakes, heights, and enclosed places.

For example, have you ever heard of *triskaidekaphobia*? It's the fear of the number 13, and, as with other phobias, a person's triskaidekaphobia may be linked to an experience in the past. For example, if you had a bad experience in a house whose street number was 1313, you might link that experience to the number 13 years later—and find yourself fearing or avoiding it. To an outsider, it might seem unreasonable to be afraid of something that absolutely can't hurt you, but because of past experiences, things can develop meanings and associations (like Pavlov's bell) that feel very real but are not actually dangerous in the present.

For example, Kate, who was once attacked by a tiger, finds that she is afraid of being attacked again and constantly scans the horizon—no matter where she may be—to make sure no tigers are around, and to ensure that she will not be attacked again. When she saw an orange carpet, she felt intense fear, even though she knows that a carpet can't hurt her. In fact, every time she sees the color orange, it serves as a trigger for anxiety and she may feel the same sensations she felt when she was actually being attacked!

When a phobia develops, it is hard to shake. Once an association is made and a network of fear is built, a person may begin to avoid things that might trigger those sensations. In the case of the woman and the tiger, anything the color orange provoked intense anxiety.

Phobia Treatment: Systematic Desensitization and In Vivo Exposure

One of the most widely used treatments for phobias is an exposure-based treatment called *systematic desensitization*. In this treatment, people make a list of the least to most scary aspect of a phobia. This list is called a hierarchy (e.g., like a ladder from the lowest stress to highest stress). For example, if someone was afraid of mice, the least scary rung on the ladder may be a cartoon picture of a mouse and the scariest rung would be holding a live mouse. Steps in between may be a realistic picture of the mouse, a mouse in a cage in another room, and a mouse in a cage in the same room. Before any exposure, people are taught relaxation skills. Then they are exposed to the lowest step on the hierarchy—one they can comfortably tolerate (e.g., by relaxing) then can move on to the next step. In order to reduce or extinguish fear related to a specific phobia, people learn to cope and overcome their fear at each step of the hierarchy.

After sexual trauma, many people fear going to certain places or doing certain activities that they once may have enjoyed. *In vivo exposure* is a process of direct exposure to the feared object, place, or situation. Participants make a hierarchy of experiences that cause them anxiety (similar to systematic desensitization). Using a scale from 0 to 100 anchored at three points—from a completely safe and relaxed situation (0) to the most terrifying situation (100), and then something in the middle (50)—participants rank their list of situations that they avoid. Starting with something low on the list, participants then go to the place and breathe until the anxiety subsides. This type of exposure teaches participants that they are okay and the feared places are not dangerous. Remember in Chapter 2 how new experiences change the neural networks?

For example, if someone was assaulted at a park and the person develops a phobia of parks, then going to a park or, better yet, going to the park where the assault occurred, could be helpful to confront the associated fears. (You can do this in a gentle way with support.)

Agoraphobia and Social Phobias

When a traumatic event occurs, it is natural to want to avoid things that feel dangerous in order to stay safe. However, like Pavlov's dogs responded to a bell, it is also natural to have conditioned anxiety reactions to things that are not actually dangerous but just have been paired with the trauma. This may lead to avoiding people, places, or even going out of one's house. *Agoraphobia* is the fear of leaving familiar places and being in open spaces. *Social phobia* is a fear of being in social situations.

As with other phobias, exposure can be helpful in alleviating anxiety related to leaving the house or being in social settings. While some exposure requires exposure to real life (in vivo), other kinds of exposure can be practiced using imagery. Once you can imagine entering into an anxiety-producing situation without feeling fear, then you can take small steps to confront the situation.

What scene might make you nervous or cause a feeling of panic? Imagine entering into that scene—and not only getting through it, but feeling victorious as a result! What skills might you need to handle the situation for a positive outcome? What might you do to ensure your safety? What positive self-talk and relaxation technique could you use to help you through the experience?

_____

_____

_____

When you are ready to try exposure to live situations, such as going to a party if you usually avoid groups of people, it is helpful to work slowly and with small goals, such as staying at the party for a few minutes to start. If you feel anxious leaving your house, you can simply try opening the front door and standing inside to see how that feels. Eventually, you can make your way outside of the door onto the front step, and, later on, down the front path. The point is to work through your fear and anxiety, repeating the action until you no longer feel uncomfortable. With each step, it is important to keep in mind the idea that the anxiety is temporary and will pass, and to achieve success each time you do something, however small, to confront that fear.

When working on confronting phobias, it is also useful to make sure you know you have a way out of the situation. In other words, it may be more comfortable to attend a social function if you know you can always leave, and have a plan to do so. For example, you can drive yourself or plan on taking public transportation rather than relying on someone else for a ride if you feel the need to go. It is advised that you start with nonthreatening situations and work up to more challenging situations. This is especially important because if you choose a situation that is too distressing, it may be discouraging and you will be less likely to make future attempts.

For example, Carla, who fears crowds, decided to "jump in" and go to the state fair for her first social outing in many years. Not surprisingly, this was a poor choice and set her up for failure: She had a panic attack and had to leave early. Afterward, she felt discouraged and the experience generated a host of negative, self-deprecating thoughts and discounted the coping skills that she was learning. The lesson? Set yourself up for success with small, attainable goals!

Another strategy is the "buddy system." Go outside or to a social event with a friend to help build self-confidence. When you are on your outing, there may be opportunities to practice being alone, such as when the friend goes to the restroom. If you become anxious, you can always use the COPE strategy. In fact, if you know you are going to be in a situation that may produce anxiety, it's a good idea to create a COPE card *before* you go. The following is an example of how to fill out a COPE card.

Cleansing breath: Take several slow, deep breaths, exhaling completely.

Observation: *Watch the sensations and thoughts come and go.*

Positive self-talk: *"I can get through this." "I'm okay right now." "I can always leave." "Just go a bit further." "I am doing a great job coming this far."*

Explanation: *"I am only responding to thoughts of fear. Nothing bad is actually happening right now."*

You can fill out your own COPE card:

COPE Card

Cleansing breath: Take several slow, deep breaths, exhaling completely.

Observation: _____

Positive self-talk: _____

Explanation: _____

Wouldn't it be nice to manage and reduce the stress and anxiety associated with phobias and triggers? You can do this . . . you can COPE!

Did You Know . . .

Deliberate distraction is another technique that can help lower anxiety. Deliberate distraction means doing something that distracts you from anxiety. So, for example, if you were anxious about going outside, you could *sing to yourself* while you open the door. It is very difficult to feel anxious and sing at the same time. This can direct your attention away from feeling panic or fear, increasing your success!

ANXIETY WORKSHEET

Use the following worksheet to (1) create a relaxing place, (2) identify your fears, (3) gain perspective, and (4) then go back to your relaxing place. Be sure to start with something small and easy to do. The idea is to slowly master these fears, not overwhelm you! When you feel anxious, bring your mind back to a peaceful and happy thought. Remember, you are okay . . . if you feel anxious, it will pass; it is only temporary and triggered by a thought. You can change your thoughts at any time and that will help you feel better. The idea is to toggle between fear and relaxation . . . eventually being able to hold both at the same time until the fear dissipates.

Step One: Identifying a Relaxing Place

Think of an image that makes you feel happy, safe, and relaxed. Maybe you want to be in a beautiful and fragrant garden surrounded by colorful flowers and butterflies. Or maybe you prefer a white sandy beach, blue skies, and the soothing sound of waves gently washing onto the shore. Or maybe you would like to be lounging on a soft chaise longue by a crystal blue swimming pool. Think of an image, your "happy place," where you feel safe and relaxed. It is best if you can think of a sight, sound, smell, feeling, and taste associated with your image. Be specific and make it as vivid as possible.

_____

_____

_____

_____

_____

Step Two: Identifying Triggers

What are some of your triggers? Think of sights, smells, feelings, sounds, tastes, or combinations of these things. Identify phobias. Do you think you have any phobias? If so, what most frightens you and is something that you avoid?

_____

_____

_____

_____

_____

_____

_____

Step Three: Gaining Perspective

Is it possible to take a step back and remove the meaning or association of trauma with the trigger or phobia? Can the thing simply be just a thing? Or a thought just be a thought? Try observing the feared object from afar, breathe and relax, and imagine it being far away, while you are safe and comfortable. It cannot harm you in any way.

Step Four: Go Back to Your Relaxed Imagery

Now imagine somewhere beautiful and safe that makes you feel happy, such as a tropical beach, by a beautiful waterfall, or somewhere else where you feel good.

Repeat the steps until the anxiety dissipates.
Don't forget to use something that smells good if you get triggered or upset!

MORE RELAXATION SKILLS

Healthy Distraction

Distraction is particularly helpful when you are anxious and need to refocus your mind. Choose a positive activity and you will most likely feel better!

- Go for a walk
- Watch an uplifting movie
- Make a date with a friend
- Visit the puppies in a pet store
- Go to the beach
- Take a warm bubble bath
- Listen to music

- Ride a bike
- Read a good book or magazine
- Stop and smell some flowers
- Take a scenic drive
- Put on music and dance
- Go for a hike in nature
- Do a craft project
- Clean your home

Exercise

Exercise is one of the best ways to reduce stress and anxiety. It improves your mood and decreases your experience of stress. What are some fun ways to get moving? Do you like to dance, go for a walk around your neighborhood, hike in nature, or power walk in a mall?

Self-Expression

Expressing yourself is a great way to reduce stress and usually leads to immediate relief. Writing about your feelings or talking to a trusted friend or counselor can help in many ways, such as helping you feel validated, gain insights, solve problem, and release hurt and frustration. What are some other ways to express your feelings? How about through creative writing, artwork, singing, dancing, or acting?

Mindful Awareness

Mindful awareness is simply being aware of this moment, right now—feeling yourself sitting in a chair, focusing on your breath in and out of your nose, either closing your eyes or looking around the room, and seeing all that is around you.

The point of this exercise is to be here in the present moment and not allow your thoughts to take you somewhere else. If you notice your thoughts going into a memory from the past, or worry in the future, or if you notice yourself thinking about what you are going to do after group, or judging yourself or someone else in the room, gently redirect your thoughts to simply observing and experiencing this moment. Breathe and just be. Right now, you are okay, you are safe, and just being. Allow yourself to relax into this moment . . . into this breath.

One-Minute Mindfulness Exercise

For this exercise, the group is instructed to start with a *signal breath*, followed by 1 minute of mindful awareness, ending with a *cleansing breath*.

The secret of health for both mind and body is not to mourn for the past, not to worry about the future, or not to anticipate troubles, but to live in the present moment wisely and earnestly.
—*Buddha*

ANXIETY LOG

Pay attention to the next time you experience anxiety due to a trigger, intrusive thought, panic attack, or phobia. Welcome them . . . as they are opportunities to practice your new skills and increase your awareness about yourself. Manage these occurrences with COPE until the anxiety subsides. Each event is an opportunity to learn from your experience. By becoming aware, you can make conscious choices. Over time you may notice a decrease in the frequency, amplitude, and duration of the anxiety!

Date	What happened?	My coping response.	How well did it work?

CHAPTER 4 SUMMARY POINTS

- What are "triggers" of anxiety? A trigger can be anything that serves as a reminder of the trauma that has been experienced, such as a sight, sound, smell, taste, feeling, or object.

- Neutral sights, smells, sounds, and tastes that occurred at the time of the trauma can be associated or paired with trauma. Those previous neutral sights, smells, sounds, tastes, and feelings are now triggers or reminders of trauma and can produce anxiety responses all on their own.

- People with PTSD may have problems regulating their "fight, flight, or freeze" system. They may have an inability to calm down from stress. This combined with being more easily triggered by stress, over time, causes people with PTSD to feel drained and exhausted. This may result in a general numbing response to stress as well as moments of intense stress.

- A simple, effective strategy to deal with triggers or anxiety is "COPE." C stands for *cleansing breath*, O stands for *observation*, P stands for *positive self-talk*, and E stands for *explanation*.

- Panic attacks are a type of anxiety characterized by sudden overwhelming periods of anxiety with several physical symptoms including shortness of breath, dizziness, and heart palpitations. A phobia is an intense fear of a very specific item.

- Name three relaxation tools that you can use:

_____

_____

_____

Did You Know . . .

Fear is just a thought. It is not actually happening. It's just a thought using your imagination, thinking about "what if this happens" . . . but it is not actually happening. Similarly, you can imagine being on a beach feeling happy and relaxed. Yes, that, too, is not actually happening, but it sure does feel better!

Anger and Resentment

Consider how much more you suffer from your anger and grief, than from those very things for which you are angry and grieved.

—*Marcus Antonius*

- *Opening exercises: Expressing with the body*
  (Day 1: Statues, Day 2: Sculpting)
- *Closing exercises: Quiet music and introduction to mindful awareness*
  (Day 1: Introduction to mindful awareness and listen to music, Day 2: Listen
  to music)

DEALING WITH ANGER AND RESENTMENT

Anger is a natural emotion in response to something that is wrong, a violation, or something that should not have happened. While anger may spur people into taking positive action, it can also negatively dominate people's lives, intruding on experiencing joy or pleasure. In this chapter we will explore the nature of trauma-related anger and resentment, examine the impact it may have on your life, and learn about coming to terms with it.

Anger is also a powerful "umbrella" emotion, which means it may be "covering" or even blocking other feelings. When you are really angry, can

you feel other emotions or does the anger tend to dominate and mask other feelings? Sometimes people are not aware that they even have other feelings. Others know they are angry but have difficulty expressing it. Because anger is such a powerful emotion, it is important to explore what it is and how it can be useful.

Anger can be an umbrella emotion covering a host of emotions such as sadness, fear, hopelessness, unmet needs, disappointments, anxiety, and hurt.

THE DOWNS AND UPS OF ANGER

Anger is an indicator that something is not right, a boundary has been crossed, or a violation has occurred. Anger tells us that there has been a wrong or injustice. While it is not uncommon to think of anger as "negative" or "bad," the truth is it can also be helpful and constructive. Anger can motivate us to change a situation—from working for social justice to creating and holding necessary interpersonal boundaries. Anger is a potent motivator, and can be a positive force.

Can you think of an example of how anger can be *productive*?

_____

_____

_____

At the same time, some forms of anger can be highly destructive, to the point that they overwhelm other feelings and impact or even destroy relationships, health, and property.

Can you think of an example of how anger can *destructive*?

_____

_____

_____

Has anger ever had a negative impact on your life? How might it have affected your relationships, health, or well-being?

_____

_____

There are many ways to experience and express anger: Some people cry, withdraw, or grow silent, while others shout, hit, or throw things. Physically, anger is a stress response similar to the "fight or flight" response discussed in Chapter 4. People may feel their skin flush (i.e., get hot or red), muscles pump up, fists or jaw clench, and have a surge of energy and intense focus.

How do you know when you are angry? What signs or symptoms do you feel when you are angry?

_____

_____

RAGE

Not all anger is alike. We will discuss two common forms of anger: rage and resentment. Rage is typically impulsive, aggressive, loud, hot, and intense. It can be part of a cycle characterized by an explosive fury that peaks and then subsides, followed by calm periods. Rage may be triggered or "set off" by any number of things, usually a perceived injustice or slight. The fury of rage can be frightening for both the person experiencing it and for others around him or her. It may lead to regrettable behavior, such as fights or self-destructive acts. Rage may encompass many different feelings, including a sense of being out of control or being misunderstood or disrespected. If you have a tendency to rage, one question would be to find out what you are really feeling. Is there a deep hurt or unresolved perception of threat or danger from the past? In other words, why do you have rage—how does it "make sense" given your past? Is it in some ways protective for you but in other ways destructive? If on the other hand you are on the other side of the continuum and avoid anger, what may happen if you express it? Are you afraid that anger will become rage? Is this related to your past? Please take a moment and explore the answers to these questions for yourself.

Writing exercise: **What do you feel about rage?**

_____

_____

_____

_____

_____

_____

_____

_____

Anger in Action: Mad and MADD

When Candy Lightner's 13-year-old daughter was struck and killed by a drunk driver—his fifth offense in 4 years—her outrage and grief prompted her to take action. In 1980, she founded MADD: Mothers Against Drunk Driving. Today, MADD is the country's largest nonprofit working to combat drunk driving and underage drinking, with the goal of ending this danger. Thanks to the anger of Candy and other women working together, MADD has successfully promoted safer roads through legislation that takes action against drunk drivers.

RESENTMENT

Resentment is very different from rage. While rage is explosive and expressed outwardly, resentments are subtle and held internally. Rage is reactive and triggered in the moment, while resentments are rooted in past events, circumstances, and feelings. However, they may get complicated because old resentments may replay themselves with new people or situations. Old resentments don't just go away; they smolder like coals on a fire that has already burned out. It may appear that the fire is gone because there are no longer outward flames (rage and anger), but the heat from the coals is just as hot, and possibly more intense, than the actual fire. Similarly, resentments can be just as intense as rage but without the outward expression. Unfortunately, resentments, like smoldering coals, can stay burning inside of you, potentially wreaking havoc on your life.

Resentment is unresolved anger resulting from not addressing angry feelings associated with hurt or injustice from the past. It may include replaying a feeling or repeatedly going over an event or situation in your mind, reviewing the hurt and intensifying the feelings of anger. People do this type of replaying of events because they are seeking resolution. They can't believe it happened and they feel the injustice should be addressed. Although some injustices can fade away into the past, others seem to stay very much alive and in the present.

> It's amazing how a traumatic memory can remain very much alive. It doesn't behave like a regular memory. The memory doesn't decay.
> —*Alain Brunet, M.D.*

And while resentment may seem less negative and powerful than rage, it can be just as destructive and self-destructive. Resentment may be directed toward a particular person or event, but can then be displaced onto other people in unrelated situations. Once resentment has been held for a prolonged period of time, it can begin to feel "normal" and can be difficult to dislodge. For some people, resentment leads to irritability and could flip, without warning, into rage. For example, some people may feel edgy, impatient, or as though they have a "short fuse." They may withdraw from others, be preoccupied with angry thoughts, and feel generally disgruntled because of unresolved resentments. What do you think trying to have an intimate relationship with someone who has a lot of resentments would be like?

How do you think resentment could lower your emotional reserves and affect your relationships or ability to tolerate stress? Is it possible to have true intimacy with someone who is resentful?

_____

_____

_____

How do you feel when you hold onto resentment?

_____

_____

_____

As stated, resentments are often fueled by events of the past—and sometimes the distant past. For example, let's say a friend breaks a date for something that you were looking forward to doing, and you cannot let go of your hurt and anger and don't understand why. Chances are that your feelings may be influenced by past experiences of feeling betrayed, disregarded, abused, or other strong feelings, and that the recent incident serves as a trigger to elicit and revive these feelings. Something in the current interaction may have triggered hurt feelings that never got addressed from the past to all of a sudden "wake up" and grab your attention. To understand resentment, it is helpful to look into those old feelings and incidents to detect why and how you may feel.

Your resentments may focus on *people*, including the perpetrator of a crime committed against you and/or others who may have been involved in a traumatic event; members of your family of origin and childhood; people with whom you were involved in romantic relationships; people who you know or have known through work; casual acquaintances; people you have known through activities or professional services, such as doctors, lawyers, and other professionals; and police officers and/or others in positions of power.

You might also have feelings of resentment directed at *institutions*, such as a school, religious institutions, the military, marriage, the criminal justice system, the foster care/child protective care system, government, society, and others. Think about the various things that you may feel do not live up to your expectations, or that continue to bother you.

Writing exercise: **Exploring your resentments. Do you have resentments or unresolved anger from the past? Is there a wrong that never got resolved or addressed?**

_____

_____

_____

_____

_____

_____

_____

_____

_____

_____

_____

_____

_____

When unexamined, resentment can dictate the way you live and hold you back from engaging with others fully and happily. How does this happen? Resentment toward an individual or about past injustices allows him or her to control you, and become ever-present in your thoughts and intrude on your contentment. Regardless of the situation, when resentment is present, that individual—and the lingering anger you harbor—is never far away. In fact, it can color your view of the world, and may be present from the moment you wake up until the time you go to sleep. Resentment, when harbored for years, can become your master.

> Resentment is like taking poison and hoping the other person dies.
> —*St. Augustine*

WHY HOLD ONTO RESENTMENT?

If resentment is clearly bad for us, why do we hold onto hurts and resentment? There are many reasons: First of all, there is a desire to make things right. By reviewing past hurts or wrongs, there is a belief that eventually something will make it right. Maybe it will go away if you think about it enough. Or maybe if you tell the past issue to others they too will become angry and onboard with your feelings, and somehow this will validate you and relieve the feelings. Maybe this will make it right. Secondly, reviewing the issue justifies the anger and resentment. You are supposed to be angry because this happened to you, and to not be angry somehow diminishes the significance of the wrong. Sometimes people feel that if they don't keep the injustice "awake and alive" then it would be like saying it never happened, that it didn't matter, was insignificant, or was really not that bad. This belief will absolutely interfere with any attempts to let go of anger and resentment! Instead, "being right" may become more important than seeking an alternative to feeling angry. This of course is ineffective and only puts *you* in jail, waiting for someone else to be punished!

Because there was no justice, it may be difficult to come to terms with what happened in the past, and maybe you don't know any other way to deal with the pain. And so, through resentment, you may end up experiencing pain again and again, hoping that by doing so justice will somehow be served.

It is well known that many events of MST are never reported, and even those that are do not necessarily get handled in a satisfying way. MST in itself is a terrible wrong, but on top of that, when you consider how it was handled (or not) and the impact it had on your health, career, and the rest of your life while the perpetrator seemed to get away with it with no consequences is enough to evoke fury in anyone. It can feel like everyone around you—and the whole world—denies MST, and denies your experience. Of course you are angry! Why wouldn't you be?

So first we must identify and acknowledge the anger. Only then can we explore ways to release anger and resentments without diminishing the terrible wrongs and injustices that have happened, and without compromising your sense of being right or justified in your reactions.

Just for the record, what happened to you *was wrong*! It was absolutely wrong! You have the right to be angry! *And* you have the right to be happy. Haven't you suffered enough from the wrong? Don't you also deserve to be happy and free? There is a price to pay for being angry—the question is this: "Is it worth it?" Because the reality is that your anger, no matter how justified, does not punish the perpetrator. It only hurts you.

EXPLORING YOUR ANGER

To understand anger, it can be helpful to explore the ways that you may be "triggered" and your associated thoughts, feelings, and physical sensations.

Anger Trigger

What types of things cause you to feel angry? Are you reminded of something that occurred in the past?

_____

_____

Anger Level

How angry do you feel when this happens, on a scale of 1 to 10? Identify your feelings, with 1 being slightly annoyed to 10 meaning extreme rage.

_____

_____

Physical Response

How does your body respond when you are feeling angry? Does your body feel muscle tension, are you breathing more quickly, or do you have a sensation of your blood pressure rising?

_____

_____

Response

When you felt anger in the past, how did you respond? Did you lash out at someone, walk away to cool down, get quiet and withdrawn, or have an outburst? How would you like to respond in the future?

_____

_____

Did You Know . . .

Resentment isn't just bad for your mind and your relationships—it may also be harmful to your health! The stress of harboring resentment may increase your risk for heart disease, stroke, high blood pressure, and other problems.

A WORD ON FORGIVENESS

Forgiveness is a topic that comes up frequently in a course on healing sexual trauma and in particular when discussing anger and justice. Participants may ask, "Why can't I just forgive my perpetrator?" and instead of feeling relief they feel added pressure, self-blame, and frustration.

First of all, what does it mean to forgive? Typically if someone hurts another, usually unintentionally, when he or she becomes aware of it the person may apologize and ask for forgiveness (e.g., "Will you forgive me?"). This is a request to (1) pardon the transgression, (2) release the anger and hurt, and (3) mend a relationship. It may be confusing if pardoning, releasing anger, and mending relationships are all lumped together as one term (forgiveness), instead of seeing these as separate independent actions (e.g., you can release anger without pardoning or mending). And MST is a different situation than in the example above. MST is a deliberate act and the perpetrator may have no intention of apologizing or making amends.

If people feel compelled to forgive, this should be done after they have had a chance to acknowledge their feelings and heal. If this is attempted prematurely, it is like putting a Band-Aid on top of a gunshot wound without removing the bullet. The injury will fester and not heal properly. Also, it is not a requirement to forgive in order to heal. It is actually the opposite—when you have healed, then you can consider if you do or don't want to forgive (i.e., pardon, release, and mend). *It is also absolutely possible to let go of the anger, hurt, and resentment, and still acknowledge that what happened to you was very wrong and unacceptable . . . and always will be.* The fact is *some acts are unforgiveable.*

Have you noticed that sexual trauma and abuse survivors are often asked to forgive their perpetrators, but other victims of crimes are not asked to do this? We have a judicial system that punishes criminals—not forgives them! So why are victims of sexual trauma and abuse so readily asked to forgive? One of the reasons is that most perpetrators are known to the victim and are part of their social network (e.g., family, work, or military environment). Those who are asking for "forgiveness" may actually be asking for the victim not to upset the social situation, to be quiet, and to minimize the event. For example, asking someone to forgive an uncle for his molestation so she doesn't "ruin" Thanksgiving dinner is dismissing and could be experienced as further emotional abuse. It would be horribly unfair to ask a victim to pretend it is okay when the rest of the family denies it. If there was genuine acknowledgement, responsibility, and apology in this family, then forgiveness can be a potentially healthy response.

"Letting it go" in the above example is a game of denial to serve others in a social situation. But letting go of hurt and anger in order to free yourself is about serving you—freeing you, healing you, and allowing you to live your life. It has nothing to do with the perpetrator . . . nor is it done for the benefit of others. You can let go of your anger because that is what is good for you, without denying, minimizing, or pardoning what has happened.

For some, forgiveness is a spiritual choice and the goal may be to "forgive the sinner but not the sin"—or even "pray for the sinner." This may work if the person is ready and able to forgive on a spiritual level, but, again, this is recommended only after addressing feelings on a human level. There may be a time and place for both.

What are your thoughts and feelings about forgiveness?

_____

_____

> Hurt leads to bitterness, bitterness to anger, travel too far on that road and
> the way is lost.
> —*Terry Brooks*

CHARTING ANGER

One method for expressing your angry feelings is to chart them. This method may be more effective if you can identify very specific people or events as the cause of your anger. To chart your anger, take a piece of paper and turn it so that it is horizontal. Make three columns at the top of the sheet and write: What happened? What did I expect should have happened? How did I respond? Fill in the columns, adding as many entries as you want. You will realize that at the core of every upset is a thwarted expectation (something should or shouldn't have happened).

Automatic Writing

There are many ways to write about feelings of anger. The simplest is to list every single thing—including people, places, things, and situations . . . *anything* that you feel angry about. Use the line, "I'm angry because. . . ." Try to fill the entire page. Don't worry about your spelling or punctuation, or whether the things that you write make sense or are in a logical sequence. This method, sometimes called "automatic writing," helps you vent your feelings. When you do automatic writing, try not to stop. Keep going until you have exhausted your thoughts involving anger.

Writing exercise: **I'm angry because . . . (or what really makes me angry is . . .)**

_____

_____

_____

_____

_____

_____

_____

_____

_____

_____

_____

_____

_____

_____

_____

_____

_____

_____

After writing about anger, consider these questions: What seems to be the core of your anger? What is being triggered? Are there other feelings that come up once you acknowledge the anger?

POETIC JUSTICE

The root cause of anger for many people is a lingering feeling of injustice. As already mentioned, many incidents of MST are not handled well. People may feel resentment because there was no legal justice for an illegal act. They may hold onto a hope for some sort of "payback," such as revenge or compensation for what occurred to them. At the very least, wouldn't it be nice to get a sincere apology for being so wronged? However, the desire for closure in the form of acknowledgment or validation from others can get so great that it may become confused with healing. It enables the perpetrator to continue to bother you, and keeps you engaged in that struggle. Years can pass by while you are waiting for justice that may never happen.

Therefore, it is important to separate your healing and freedom—which is within your control—from acknowledgment from the outside world, which often is not. Thinking your healing will _only_ come if you get justice puts you in a holding position, waiting . . . maybe for your whole lifetime. The desire for justice may get in the way of feeling more positive or being more productive or living fully in the present. Holding out for fantasy outcomes—whether revenge or an apology—can continue the cycle of bitterness, interfering with your life and certainly with your happiness.

How does one come to terms with the fact that bad things happen to good people, and that bad people may get away with bad actions? In order to move on and heal, let's consider the concept of *poetic justice*.

What is poetic justice? Poetic justice is the idea that people's actions are interconnected to other actions. Like the concept of "karma" or the "boomerang effect," poetic justice is the idea that what goes around comes around—and that eventually a person's behavior, good or evil, returns to him or her. It also includes the idea that people are consistent: If they have done something bad in the past, chances are that they will repeat that behavior—and they will suffer the natural consequences of their own behavior. The idea of poetic justice suggests that perpetrators of trauma will repeat their patterns, and eventually will pay for their actions. We may not know when or how this will occur, but accepting the idea of poetic justice means that they will get their just deserts and you don't have to put your life on hold waiting for it.

How does it feel if you consider this: *"Somehow, some way, somewhere, people reap the natural consequences of their behaviors"*? People know when they commit a crime like sexual trauma. Perpetrators know what they did, even if they pretend they don't . . . even if they convince others that they didn't do it, even if they try to blame their victims . . . they know. They know exactly what they did. If they feel guilty, ashamed, or afraid of being caught, that may weigh on their conscience, or affect their health and well-being.

Example: A female veteran was terrified because she ran into her active duty perpetrator twice when she was out shopping at a nearby base. When asked about his reaction, she said the first time he was stunned and didn't move. The second time he saw her, he ran away. She realized that she was so focused on her own fear of him that she hadn't noticed he was actually afraid of her! He was afraid that she would report him and he would get in trouble. He knew what he did and has to live with the fear of consequences. Perpetrators know exactly what they did. They may try to justify their behavior or lie to themselves and others, but, nonetheless, they have to live with themselves—knowing that what they did was wrong.

> **Nothing is more wretched than the mind of a man conscious of guilt.**
> *—Titus Maccius Plautus*

If a perpetrator does not feel guilt or remorse, then most likely his own nasty behavior will catch up to him. This is not to be confused with wishing ill on people or wanting revenge; the idea of poetic justice is that people's own behavior will lead to natural consequences—that they create! Since perpetrators will create their own consequences, you don't have to.

In addition, eventually everyone has to come to terms with "their maker." Nobody knows what lies beyond this life, and people have many different beliefs about it. But sure enough everyone will pass from this life and maybe justice will be served in a way that we cannot comprehend. Although we can only speculate about what could happen to perpetrators, the point is you don't have to be the holder of the anger anymore. The wrongs others have committed are theirs, not yours! They will incur their own consequences. The burden is on them.

Many people who have survived MST and other sexual traumas find that the idea of poetic justice can help them come to terms with the nagging thought that perpetrators "got away" with doing something terrible. While it is not the same thing as direct "payback," believing in poetic justice may help you find peace in the present, because it allows you to let go of thoughts of the past. With poetic justice, you no longer need to be the "jail keeper" of your perpetrator in your mind or heart.

> Letting go helps us to live in a more peaceful state of mind and helps restore our balance. It allows others to be responsible for themselves and for us to take our hands off situations that do not belong to us. This frees us from unnecessary stress.
> —*Melody Beattie*, The Language of Letting Go

Did You Know . . .

It is incredibly aggravating to think that the perpetrator of a crime against you got away with it—and may deny that it ever happened. Though you may not personally be able to do anything about the perpetrator, with poetic justice, somehow, somewhere, some way that person's negativity will come back to him or her. You don't have to keep waiting for justice. You deserve to be free and have a life of happiness.

FINDING FREEDOM THROUGH "RADICAL ACCEPTANCE"

Finding freedom from resentment can begin with the concept of "radical acceptance," a term coined by Marsha Linehan (1993). What is radical acceptance? Radical acceptance is the idea of accepting what was and what is, and not what we wish it were, or would have been, or could have been. It means being clear-eyed about what happened by breaking the silence and telling our truths—and accepting the fact that we cannot change certain things. It means acknowledging that we have what we have, and that as much as we might want to change something, it cannot and will not change.

One way of looking at radical acceptance is to imagine you have a blue pen—you do not have a red one or a yellow one; what you have is blue. No matter how much you wish the blue one was red, it is still blue. And no matter how angry you may be—you may hate it, resent it, think it is not fair, and feel all sorts of emotions about it—it will still be a blue pen. What is, is. What was, was. You can't change the color of the pen.

When it comes to trauma, radical acceptance means coming to terms by accepting what is and what was, without resisting, avoiding, or holding onto anger. While the concept certainly does not mean condoning traumatic events, it does accept the fact that they occurred. Radical acceptance is a conscious decision to accept the fact of what happened—and know it cannot be changed, as much as you might wish it could be different. Radical acceptance is a form of empowerment, clarifying the past and putting us in control of how we proceed in the future. And it can be key to stopping the issue or event from being the source of anger and resentment.

> Some of us think holding on makes us strong, but sometimes it is letting go.
> —*Herman Hesse*

Did You Know . . .

Some physical states may trigger resentment, just as they trigger other feelings. If you are feeling especially resentful, check in with yourself to see if you might be hungry, thirsty, or tired—these are physical states that can influence how you are feeling.

REDIRECTING ENERGY

Imagine that each of us has 100 circuits of "life force energy" flowing through us, like beautiful rays of light. Now, imagine taking 10—or 20, or 30, or more—of those lovely energy strands and plugging them into anger or resentment. Carolyn Myss, author of *Anatomy of the Spirit* (1997), describes how we may "spend" our energy unwisely on unhappy or traumatic memories in this way. When we "plug in" to something that does not help us, it takes away the energy for more positive things in our lives. As one trauma survivor noted, "With all these light strands being plugged into the past, it's like we are living in the dark!" By "unplugging" our energy from anger and resentment toward others, we may redirect our energy to ourselves—and have more "light" in our lives.

What happened was not fair, it was not right, and should never, ever have happened. . . . But it did. It may be challenging to accept that this is what happened, especially when you know it was so wrong and should not have happened. It is tragic. But holding onto anger only poisons you and does nothing to help the situation. This is where "poetic justice" is so helpful—somehow, somewhere, some way, people reap what they sow. Now it is time for you to be free! Can you accept that what is, is what is, and let go, unplug from the past, and release your anger?

> *Don't let a wrong from the past rob you of your precious life anymore. Breathe . . . and know that when you let it go, you free yourself for better things to come!*

Mindful Awareness

Mindful awareness, or "mindfulness," is a practice of "being present" popularized by Jon Kabat-Zin who applied this technique in the Western medical field. He was able to demonstrate that people with moderate to severe psoriasis who practiced mindfulness with their light treatment cleared their skin four times faster than people who just got light treatment alone (Kabat-Zin et al., 1998)!

How do you practice mindfulness with *open eyes*? It can start with simply sitting in a chair and looking around the room. Just being in this moment and focusing on your experience. Place your feet on the ground, hands resting in your lap, and notice the sights, sounds, and smells that you may be experiencing. You can also focus on your breathing ... focusing on the sensations of the breath going in and out of the nose, noticing the rise and fall of the chest. In this moment, nothing else exists—just here and now.

CHAPTER 5 SUMMARY POINTS

- What happened to you was WRONG, WRONG, WRONG! It was absolutely unfair and not your fault. You have every right to be angry because of how it affected your life. You have every right to feel frustrated and resentful because justice was never served.

- It is important to acknowledge your feelings and know that others acknowledge them as well.

- You also deserve to be happy and have the life you want to live from this day forward. *Poetic justice* helps release the anger by believing that in some way, somewhere, somehow, people will receive the natural consequences of their own behavior. They will get what they deserve because of their own doing.

- *Radical acceptance* is acknowledging what happened, and that now it is in the past. It just is . . . and you can't change it.

- Are you ready to wipe your hands and say enough is enough?! Is it time to get angry at the anger and make a decision to be done—with it all? When you are ready, you can reclaim your life and work toward sustainable, authentic happiness.

Remembering and Understanding Trauma

6

> Memories can be sad, but sometimes can also save you.
> —*Takayuki Ikkaku, Arisa Hosaka, and Tishihiro Kawabata*

- *Opening exercises: Introducing sound*
  (Day 1: Conductor, Day 2: Circular rhythms)
- *Closing exercises: Musical bells and chimes*
  (Day 1: Singing bowl and chimes, Day 2: Singing bowl and chimes)

REMEMBERING TRAUMA

The purpose of remembering trauma is to help you get free from the past. Memories, though difficult at times, can help you understand what feelings, images, and other aspects of trauma you might still be "plugged into"—causing nightmares, triggers, panic, and the urge or tendency to avoid your life. Now you can explore what is at the root of these feelings and address them. Memories may be experienced in many ways, including full recall, partial recall (remembering certain things but unable to recall others), and very little or no recall at all. Each way of experiencing memories is normal and should not raise concern.

With partial recall, some memories are detailed, vivid, and clear, while others are blurry. It is also very common to have fragments or snippets of memories, like isolated snapshots or short video clips. These may be very clear or like a dream; they may be disorganized, disjointed, out of sequence, and floating without a context owr an anchor of time or place. Some details may be exaggerated or very clear where other details are nonexistent. For many people, memories of trauma pop into their heads unexpectedly. The disorder of our memories may be overwhelming and confusing, and it may leave us "stuck" in old feelings. They may repeat, again and again.

One reason this occurs is that as an adaptive measure in times of extreme stress people can dissociate or "numb out" to distance themselves from pain. This is adaptive but can later lead to fragmented memories. When there is simply too much for the mind to process, trauma memories can get "frozen" or "put in a box" and not processed like other memories.

Remembering Events of Trauma

Do you have any of the following? Check all that apply.

❑ Full recall ❑ Partial recall ❑ No recall ❑ Pieces or flashes of recall

Do you wish you remembered more? Do you wish you remembered less? Are you happy you do or don't remember? Are you confused or unsure if your memory actually happened? Do you have lingering questions such as "Who did it?" "Why did it happen?" or "How did it happen?" All of these questions and answers are normal reactions. Some remember, others do not, and some have a combination of all the above (e.g., in the case of multiple events).

STRESS AND MEMORY

Typically, experience is remembered in a sequential format like a story with a beginning, middle, and end. This helps people organize and recall events. However, trauma memories seem to be encoded differently than regular memories. There are two central areas in the brain that have been associated with the memory of traumatic events: the hippocampus and the amygdala. The amygdala is a small part of the brain that aids in processing highly charged emotional memories. Like a fire alarm, the amygdala sounds out an alarm to the body when there is a perception of danger, activating the fight, flight, or freeze response. Remembering trauma, just like experiencing it, activates this alarm. The other part, called the hippocampus, gives memories time, space, and context so that they can be recalled in a sequence. However, those with PTSD seem to have suppressed hippocampus activity and the traumatic event is prevented from being processed. Instead, the memory floats without context and trips the alarm every time something triggers recall of the memory.

By examining memories, we can begin to gain perspective, add context, and help the memories become processed like nontraumatic memories. We will seek to objectively examine the many facets of trauma, exploring how events occurred and considering concepts such as justice and blame. This will build a framework for remembering and a context for healing—finally setting free what has remained stuck, unprocessed, or haunting.

Did You Know . . .

It is *not* necessary to remember absolutely everything about a traumatic event in order to process it and heal. However, it can be very healing to write or talk to a therapist about what happened, going through the details in a sequential manner. Some find great relief in this exercise, especially if they have never expressed it before. The process of writing or talking can help you gain perspective and put the memory in its proper context.

HOLOGRAPHIC MEMORY

Memory is a complex topic with many ongoing controversies in the scientific field. Historically, memory has been thought to be encoded in specific regions of the brain. However, some now believe that memory may be encoded holistically. Experience occurs with multisensory inputs (through sight, sound, smell, and touch) that are coded simultaneously. A network of neurons begins to fire, creating an electrical field. Some believe that this simultaneous firing is how experience is encoded holistically. This network explanation of memory may use holographic principles (to be explained in the next section) to store the vast amounts of information that we encounter on a daily basis. Karl Pribram, author of *Brain and Perception* (1991), has done extensive research indicating that the brain stores memories holographically and that is why a memory can be triggered by any one of the senses. Paul Peitsch (1981) conducted several experiments with salamander brains and concluded that Pribram's claim that memories do not have a specific location in the brain was correct. More recently, there is evidence that individual neurons may actually code specific information but then connect with a network of other neurons, creating a circuit of neurons. Independent circuits then connect together, forming associations. This model explains an efficient memory system for processing and retrieving information. According to this model, memory is not piecemeal (i.e., remembering only the smell of apple pie) but rather it is holistic (i.e., the smell of pie triggers sensations and associations with picnics in the park, activating sights, feelings, tastes, and emotional memories). If experience is encoded simultaneously and holistically, then if one part of an experience is recalled, other parts may also be recalled.

Another aspect of memory is that in order to organize our vast array of experience, we file memories (so to speak) through our emotions. Emotions "tag" our experiences so that when we are experiencing a certain emotion we can easily recall other experiences that are associated with the same emotion. This is similar to *state-dependent learning.* When you are in a certain emotional state you can more easily recall information that was learned in the same emotional state. It is well established that people who are depressed are more likely to remember depressing experiences than nondepressed people. When someone is grieving a loss, he or she is then more likely to remember other losses. A strong emotion will facilitate the retrieval of memories (associations) that are consistent with that emotion. Remember the string of holiday lights representing an emotion? Remembering one event is like plugging in the string of lights, and you are more likely to recall all the events on the string.

A HOLOGRAPHIC APPROACH

Sexual trauma makes an imprint on the psyche that can permeate one's very being. According to *holographic reprocessing* theory (Katz, 2005), this imprint can be thought of as a psychological "hologram." A hologram is a three-dimensional image projected from special holographic film. Similar to the holographic images in the movie *Star Wars* (1977), the image is projected from the film and appears "real." In terms of trauma, every time the hologram is activated, so are certain feelings and thoughts. These are expressed in interactions with others. These interactions repeat themselves as if you are having the same types of relationships over and over again, and yet, you may not even be aware of it! (Have you ever noticed that you have a pattern of similar types of relationships?)

Did You Know . . .

A hologram is a type of picture that is made from holographic film so that if you wave the film you see a three-dimensional image that appears to be suspended in space. The image is produced by splitting a laser beam so that one half of the light source is projected onto an object and then onto the photographic film, while the other half of the laser beam is bounced off of a mirror then on to the object and then to the film. When the two laser beams meet on the photographic film, the light waves hit and form what is called an interference pattern. This is like dropping a pebble in a pond and then dropping a second pebble in the same pond. The two pebbles create a series of concentric circles that overlap. The photographic film records this interference pattern and the image is embedded within the pattern. When the film is waved, a three-dimensional image appears to be projected in space.

To understand the difference between holographic film and other kinds of film, consider this: If you tear a picture of an apple in half, you will have two pieces of paper, each showing half an apple. If you tear holographic film with an image of an apple in half, each piece of film when waved will still project a whole apple! The whole picture of the apple is imprinted on every part of the holographic film, no matter how many pieces you make. The reason this happens is that the image in a hologram is encoded throughout the film. In other words, the whole is contained in the parts. If a piece of the film is broken off, the whole image can still be projected. Each part of the film contains information about the whole.

In the same way, when trauma occurs, it is encoded in complex networks throughout the brain. This is how the brain encodes information and experiences. The identified theme (whole) is evident across a multitude of interpersonal contacts (parts). Similarly, the effects of trauma are present across many if not all interpersonal contacts. Therefore, examining one event or one relationship reveals emotional themes that are consistent throughout a person's life. In addition, the trauma filters how a person interprets new events and new interactions, and this is projected onto others who serve to reenact these themes.

While it feels "real," the hologram is both real and an illusion at the same time. You are here in this current reality, reacting to events as they occur, and at the same time are influenced by your past reality. Your past not only filters your interpretation and reactions to current events, but also serves as a template for expectations, assumptions, and a whole array of emotional and physical reactions. *So are you responding to the here and now, or are you responding to the past?*

One participant said, "It's like if you bring all your past relationships with you and your partner brings all his past relationships with him . . . that's a lot of people in one bed!"

If you approach every new situation as if it will be a replaying of your past, what do you think you will experience? If your past influences your present, what do you think your future will look like?

_____

If you let your past influence your present, your future will look like a continuation of the past. This can be depicted as a "vector" and it looks like this:

(past) ●————————➤ (future)

However, if you are completely present in this moment—this moment, right here, right now—it would be a "point." A point looks like this:

What would your future look like from a point? *Any direction you choose.*

So, Are You Living Your Life Like a Vector or a Point?

Exercise: Choosing in the Present

Imagine you are going to buy a muffin for breakfast and you see the specials of the day are blueberry and strawberry muffins. Your task is to choose a muffin and be entirely in the present moment. Which one do you choose? Why? Let's say Mary chooses blueberry and when asked why, she says, "Because I like it!" She's asked, "How do you know you like it?" Mary responds, "Well, because I have had it in the past and I know I like blueberries." So Mary's past experience influenced her current choice. The fact is she is assuming she will like the blueberry muffin but she doesn't really know because she has not tried *this* blueberry muffin. She chooses again. She says, "I choose strawberry." She's asked why and responds, "Because I didn't choose it last time," but quickly realizes this choice is also influenced from her past.

The question is, how can Mary choose a muffin completely in the present and make choices that are here and now without expecting certain outcomes or reacting to events from the past? What are your thoughts? What would you choose and why?

_____

_____

The answer to this question is actually very simple—you choose because this is what you want to choose. You choose because you are in this moment, free and clear, and this is your choice right now. Wouldn't it be nice to retain the wisdom of your past experiences but be free enough to be completely in the present moment? That is the goal and purpose for gaining insight and identifying your own holograms. When you know what your patterns are, you have power to make choices because you choose in this present moment and are no longer automatically responding from your past. One person asked, "What if you don't ike blueberry or strawberry?" The answer: "Then choose chocolate, carrot, vanilla, or cinnamon! Or anything else of your choosing." In the present, there are an infinite number of possibilities!

So, what do you choose?

HOLOGRAPHIC REPROCESSING: AN INTRODUCTION

Holographic reprocessing, referred to as HR (Katz, 2005), involves discovering and exploring personal holograms by working to identify the patterns in your life. These experiences form the basis of limiting or negative beliefs, as well as protective behaviors or coping strategies.

For example, after an assault, people may form beliefs and perceptions about the self and others such as seeing oneself as flawed, unworthy, unlovable, or not good enough, and others and the world as unsafe, unloving, restrictive, or threatening. These perceptions set in motion thoughts, feelings, and behaviors where a person unconsciously (i.e., without awareness) replicates similar relationships that reinforce or strengthen his or her worldview (remember the neural networks that get reinforced with experience?).

These perceptions create certain patterns that repeat themselves with other people. People are not aware that they are doing this and, therefore, cannot simply "report" why they have certain relationships or even be aware that they are recreating relationships that simulate an aspect of their original trauma. However, once people are able to map their patterns they can see how their behavior makes perfect sense and at the same time continues to replicate the very pattern they may be trying to escape.

Have you ever known someone who had the same painful problems in every relationship, no matter who he or she was involved with? Through our holograms, we may unconsciously seek out something familiar and/or similar, and may actually end up repeatedly finding ourselves in situations that produce the same painful results! Like soap bubbles that are attracted and stick together, certain people may be repeatedly attracted to each other. You may find that you, too, have had the same type of relationship but with different people. Some people feel they are on a merry-go-round, repeating these relationships over and over again. What is the motor that is driving your merry-go-round? It is your hologram that has been formed, and at the root of it is a core violation that is a painful experience that has not been healed or resolved.

WHAT IS AN EXPERIENTIAL HOLOGRAM?

The term *experiential hologram* refers to a theme of experiences that emerge and are reenacted in people's relationships. Sexual trauma and abuse are both events that occurred with another person. They are, by definition, interpersonal traumas. The trauma experience as well as early learning experiences can influence future interactions with people. For example, if trauma occurred by someone the victim loved, admired, or trusted, that person may feel deeply betrayed and may have sensitivities regarding forming new loving and trusting relationships. *Experiential holograms* are formed through experiences—and they have an important adaptive function. They create a template so people respond in efficient ways according to their expectations, perceptions, and learned behaviors. It is a way to help people predict and prepare for potential danger so that they are not rejected, betrayed, or hurt again.

Situations, people, or events in the environment may trigger the activation of an *experiential hologram*. For example, a difficult relationship with someone's boss could be the type of context where an *experiential hologram* of previous difficult relationships such as with an authoritarian father, abusive husband, or inappropriate sergeant may replay itself. The *experiential hologram* becomes a three-dimensional reenactment of previous experiences in relationships. Certain outcomes are expected and because people respond according to their expectations and others in the situation respond back to their responses, the expected outcomes are often realized. Thus, *experiential holograms* are activated, reenacted, and then reinforced through new experiences, confirming the original hologram. So, although the intent is to protect oneself from re-experiencing the pain associated with the hologram, unfortunately people's assumptions and responses set them up to re-experience that pain over and over again.

EXPERIENTIAL HOLOGRAMS VERSUS TRIGGERS

One question that may arise is, how is a hologram similar or different than a trigger? In Chapter 4 we discussed triggers as a sudden recall of a feeling or image of trauma. Triggers are experienced as a flash of anxiety that may involve increased heart rate, sweat, fear, and shortness of breath. It is an anxiety response or the activation of the fight, flight, or freeze system in order to mobilize the person to get out of danger. A trigger can be a sight, sound, touch, or smell and any one of the senses can "light up" the whole memory of a traumatic event. This is the memory network that has become very efficient and highly sensitive to detecting potentially painful events.

In summary, a trigger is something that activates the fight, flight, or freeze response. The anxiety comes and goes . . . it peaks and subsides . . . it flows through you like water flows through a garden hose . . . and then the anxiety is gone.

An *experiential hologram*, on the other hand, is also a neural network but involves a complex and persistent system that includes painful experiences; ongoing perceptions about the self, others, and the world; as well as coping strategies; avoidance strategies; and motivations to meet unmet needs. When an *experiential hologram* is activated, the person mobilizes to protect against potential pain just like in a trigger, but it involves much more than the anxiety response. *Experiential holograms* involve expectations, beliefs, behaviors, memories, physical responses, feelings, and so on. *Experiential holograms* are complex because experience itself is complex.

As Seymour Epstein (2014) proposes, the experiential system processes information in a complex array of sensations and associations similar to actual experience. Likewise, *experiential holograms* are often indistinguishable from actual experience, which is why most people are unaware that they are living according to their holograms!

For example, *experiential holograms* are by their very nature interactive. Although someone may project a past experience onto a new situation, it is not exactly the same. Aspects may be the same, expectations and responses may be the same, but there is a living, interactive quality to the new experience. It is like walking onto *Star Trek*'s "Holodeck," where the hologram and live human being interact!

Experiential holograms also have no sense of time. The experiential system does not process information in a linear manner, so time as a concept does not exist in the experiential mind. If, for example, a traumatic event occurred 10, 20, or 30 years ago and an *experiential hologram* is activated, the sensations of the original trauma will be experienced as fully and completely in the present time as they were in the past. In this case, these experiences are recalled and a response to the event is reenacted. Each new experience becomes an opportunity, in a way, to rewrite or rescript the original traumatic scene. Life itself becomes the stage for the reenactment and resolution of *experiential holograms*. Because the experiential mind has no sense of time, a disconfirming experience in the present confuses the old holographic patterns. However, because people repeat the same set of responses, they appear to be stuck in repeating the same holographic patterns, reinforcing the original beliefs.

REPLAYING HOLOGRAMS

What are some of the ways you may "replay" experiences? What are some of the "themes" that come up again and again in your life? How does each related experience contain the same emotional issues? At the core, *experiential holograms* are strategies to secure basic needs of life, including love, attention, affection, self-esteem, and security. When there is a rupture or violation to one of these basic needs, inevitably a child will do whatever he or she can do to secure the need. This is how the hologram forms—to avoid pain and secure basic needs.

The child personalizes what has happened ("If it happened to me, then it must be about me") and, therefore, attempts to fix the situation by developing strategies such as being attentive to others to avoid being neglected, being perfect to avoid being criticized, or being slow to trust others to avoid being betrayed. These strategies are attempts to protect the person, but in subtle ways may be contributing to factors that set the person up for re-experiencing the very thing they want to avoid. For example, someone who feels neglected may adopt the strategy of attending to others in order to secure an attentive relationship, but this may backfire when the receiver only takes from the relationship and never gives back. Another example is that when someone seeks perfection to avoid criticism, he or she is likely to be very self-critical and never feel good enough since perfection is an unrealistic goal.

CHARACTERISTIC COPING STYLE

When a person's *experiential hologram* is activated, it means that old patterns, memories, and coping strategies also become activated. People learn characteristic strategies of coping with the difficult situation. People learn that they have to behave in certain ways in order to function (i.e., to avoid pain, to survive, to be loved, or to get attention). The characteristic coping style becomes a standard response when the hologram is engaged. Because a piece of the past is projected into the future, there is an assumption that this situation in the present will be exactly like it was in the past, and, therefore, people react to it in the same way. Their approach is consistent with their previous experience, which inadvertently helps to recreate the very experience they are trying to avoid!

A CASE EXAMPLE

Kristie went to her new boyfriend's house and was watching a football game with him and some of his friends. Meanwhile, his mother was baking cookies in the kitchen and had casually invited Kristie to join her. Kristie wanted to go make cookies with his mom but couldn't get herself to go into the kitchen. She stated that she thought about it during the whole game and even felt bored watching football. When thinking about what she experienced when she thought about going into the kitchen with his mom, she stated she felt tense even though she really wanted to join her. When she thought about going into the kitchen, she associated it with an experience with her own mother. She recalled helping her mother and feeling criticized and rejected. In the current situation, she (unconsciously) expected she would be criticized and rejected by her boyfriend's mother just as she was by her own mother, even though her boyfriend's mother had been very welcoming to her. She had an *experiential hologram* activated about unresolved feelings with her own mother and she felt rejected and inadequate without ever getting off the couch! Since her coping style was to withdraw, Kristie never went into the kitchen and was bored watching football. This reaction can actually reinforce her hologram: Maybe her boyfriend's mother wondered why Kristie didn't engage with her, or maybe she felt rejected or ignored by Kristie—this may in turn make the mother hesitant to be so welcoming in the future, which would only reinforce Kristie's fears.

Kristie was responding to her own fears from the past, which influenced how others treated her in the present, thus replicating outcomes consistent with the past. Her hologram trapped her from being in the present. Once this pattern was identified, Kristie was able to confront her negative thoughts and expectations. She was able to distinguish her feelings toward her own mother as separate from developing a relationship with her boyfriend's mother. As Kristie uses new ways to approach social situations, she will create new interactions with others with new outcomes.

Five Questions to Keep You in the Present and Out of the Holographic Trap

1. What am I feeling?

_____

_____

_____

2. Have I felt this way before?

_____

_____

_____

3. Am I currently responding to a present situation or to something from the past?

_____

_____

_____

4. If I am responding to something unique to this situation, how can I best respond?

_____

_____

_____

5. If I am responding to something from the past, how can I make it different this time?

_____

_____

_____

WRITING ABOUT TRAUMA

Is there a specific event of trauma, either sexual trauma or another event, that is particularly disturbing for you? Maybe something terrible happened and you have never told anyone about it. Or maybe you tried to tell someone and he or she didn't believe you or didn't want to hear about the details. Some people feel they can never fully recover without letting someone know or fully expressing what has happened to them. Sometimes people know what happened but they just want someone to hear their story. Writing can be a way to acknowledge and state what happened.

The act of writing, itself, can be useful because it moves unprocessed emotional feelings from the experiential system to the rational system in the brain. This process from the right to the left hemisphere helps process the feelings by anchoring the feelings into a coherent story. Many people find great relief through the process of writing. James Pennebaker (1997) conducted studies on the effects of writing. He randomly assigned students into two groups—one that wrote about their feelings, and the other that wrote about mundane topics. He found that those who wrote about their feelings had healthier immune systems and fewer doctor's visits compared to those in the other group! Unprocessed negative feelings can take a toll on the body, and writing seems to release this burden.

Writing can simply be a release—a way of getting your feelings out of your head and heart and onto a page. It creates a document that is expandable, and that can help in your process of healing. For some, writing can help organize and make sense of what happened. Experts such as PTSD authority Mardi Horowitz (1997) believe that traumatic memories that are not processed may be "frozen" as fragments. These fragments—like snapshots, scribbled short notes, and video clips jumbled together—may be difficult to understand or process. Snippets of memories may get repeated over and over, and we may experience bad feelings associated with the trauma as an attempt to fully remember what really happened. Because a memory is incomplete and incomprehensible, for some this in itself is very distressing. Therefore, for some it is helpful to fill in gaps and put those fragments into order.

Telling a trauma story, either in writing or speaking, can help "repair the narrative," meaning that it puts the fragments in order with a beginning, middle, and end. People also report that the process of telling their story helps them remember certain forgotten details that when recovered help them make sense of what happened. Telling your story can be helpful to do with a therapist or with someone else you trust. This process is not required; it is only being offered here for those who feel distressed by their disjointed memories and wish to repair their narratives. Some find it very relieving to tell their story and it helps them understand it better.

In creating a trauma narrative, ask yourself questions. How did the trauma happen? When did it happen? Who else was in the picture? What other factors were involved?

Once you have written down your story, you can go back and add details as you remember them until you are satisfied that your story has been told to the best of your ability.

Another technique is to reread your narrative until you feel you have processed the emotions or fear associated with it. This process works much like watching a horror movie many, many times. The first time you see the movie, the monster popping out of the closet is terrifying! However, the tenth time you see the movie, you know exactly what to expect, and may find yourself not only anticipating the scary moment, but yawning through it—because it is no longer so scary to you. Watching the movie many times removes the element of surprise and helps you become desensitized to the frightening feelings you may have had the first few times seeing the movie. Though your story is real, and not a movie, retelling it many times can also help you become more desensitized to its impact.

> To look backward for a while is to refresh the eye, to restore it, and to render it the more fit for its prime function of looking forward.
> —*Margaret Fairless Barber*

Optional writing exercise: **What happened and what did you feel as a result of a specific trauma experience?** You are not required to do this and this is not necessary in order to heal . . . but if you want to, and think it will be beneficial, you can write about a specific event of trauma and/or its impact on your life. Do not be surprised if it brings up old negative emotions—they will pass if you let them flow through you like water flows through a hose. Then do something positive, affirming, uplifting, and self-soothing! You might want to plan the positive activity before you start writing. Another option is to talk to a therapist.

_____

_____

_____

_____

_____

_____

_____

_____

_____

_____

_____

_____

_____

_____

_____

_____

_____

_____

_____

_____

_____

_____

_____

_____

_____

_____

_____

CHAPTER 6 SUMMARY POINTS

■ You may have full, partial, or no recall of trauma. Your memories may be clear or fuzzy. You may have a full story with beginning, middle, and end or you may only recall snippets that are disjointed and disorganized.

■ Memories can be encoded in networks of neurons in the brain. When a sight, sound, or smell reminds you of the trauma, the whole network lights up.

■ Why a hologram? The hologram is used in this theory because of three unique qualities.

  ● _First_, a hologram creates a three-dimensional image that appears to be projected into space. This gives it the illusion of being real and at the same time is actually a projection (from the past).

- *Second*, if you break off a piece of holographic film, the whole image can still be projected. Thus, each part contains information about the whole and the whole contains information about the parts. Each piece (or in this case each experience) is a whole unto itself as well as a part of a greater whole in a given context.
- *Finally*, holograms have integrity created by consistent themes that are repeated throughout a system.

- Are you living life as a vector or a point? A vector is a representation where the future looks more like a continuation of the past. A point is a representation of being in the here and now, where the future is any direction you choose!

- In order to live completely in the present, it is important to be aware of the emotional patterns or experiential hologram that may be controlling and influencing your life.

- There are five questions that can keep you in the present and out of the holographic trap:
  1. What am I feeling?
  2. Have I felt this way before?
  3. Am I currently responding to a present situation or to something from the past?
  4. If I am responding to something unique to this situation, how can I best respond?
  5. If I am responding to something from the past, then how can I make it different this time?

MINI REVIEW: SEE IF YOU CAN ANSWER THE FOLLOWING QUESTIONS

- Feelings are . . .
- Feelings flow through us like . . .
- Feelings come and they . . .
- What are three things you can do after a nightmare?
- What are three dos and don'ts of good sleep habits?
- COPE stands for . . .
- What is poetic justice?
- What is radical acceptance?

Defining Relationship Patterns

7

It is hardly possible to build anything if frustration, bitterness and a mood of
helplessness prevail.
—*Lech Walesa*

- *Opening exercises: Combining movement and sound
  (Day 1: Four-person trains, Day 2: Machine)*
- *Closing exercises: Chanting and toning
  (Day 1: Chanting CALM, Day 2: Chanting vowels and "spaceship")*

In this chapter you will explore *experiential holograms* and identify your own patterns in relationships. As discussed in the previous chapter, *experiential holograms* develop through experiences with other people. You have learned to act and react the way you do because of your environment and the relationships you have had with those around you. Through these experiences you have developed beliefs about yourself and others. Thus, your relationship patterns were formed from early experiences.

ATTACHMENT: THE FOUNDATION OF HUMAN RELATIONSHIPS

Relationships are something that develop from birth. Soon after infants are born they realize they require attention from a caretaker (typically a mother) to obtain their basic needs for life. Distinct from the basic needs of food and warmth, love also seems to be its own necessity. Experiments by Harry F. Harlow in the 1950s found that infant monkeys craved nurturing touch. He placed baby monkeys in a cage with two wire "surrogate mothers," one covered in terry cloth and the other connected to a bottle providing food. The monkeys would lean over and drink their nourishment, but they clung to their terry-cloth mothers (Harlow, 1962). Later scientists observed that babies who were not held, even when they had adequate warmth, would die because they needed the comfort of love and touch. These observations support what we call *attachment theory*. Researchers found that a good attachment or connection to one's mother or another caretaker provides a safe haven or feeling of security for a child. A secure relationship fosters healthy exploration of the world because the child knows he or she can come back to the safety of the caretaker. John Bowlby (1958, 1988) theorized that people have a biological instinct to maintain a physical connection (e.g., close proximity) to their caretaker for safety and protection. From early infancy the individual develops an internal working model of attachment that enables him or her to recognize patterns of interactions not only with the caregiver, but also generalized to others. The internal working model influences a general expectation of how others will act, and thus also influences the individual's behavior (see Wallin, 2007, for more information about attachment theory and the various researchers who helped develop it). The primary caregiver must be "good enough" for the child to feel safe and develop an internal working model of trust and safety. If the caregiver is unreliable, this leaves the child feeling insecure.

Attachment trauma results from trauma that occurs in an attachment relationship in childhood or in adulthood such as abuse, neglect, or betrayal from someone emotionally close to the victim. Trauma such as sexual trauma, caused by another person, can potentially affect one's capacity for secure attachment (e.g., evokes fear, distrust, expectation of betrayal) even if the person had a secure enough attachment in childhood. However, adult trauma may be processed through a filter of childhood attachment such that the adult trauma may be interpreted and processed in ways that are consistent with early attachment styles.

Elements for a Healthy, Secure Attachment

Secure attachment is a combination of elements: feeling loved enough and safe enough, trusting that a caretaker will hold boundaries and rules to protect you, and having enough freedom and trust in yourself and the world to go out and explore—knowing there is a safety net ready to protect and care for you.

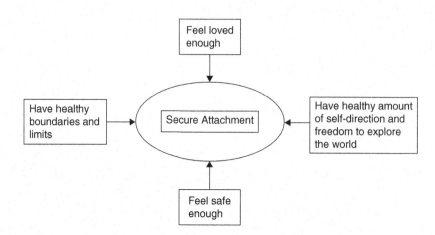

Elements for Insecure Attachment

However, if one or more of these elements is not sufficient, then it may affect the person's ability to function and form relationships. For example, if someone did not feel loved enough but had no threat of safety she may feel emptiness inside and a disconnection from others. If this is coupled with overly permissive parents (i.e., parents who did not pay attention or who allowed the child to do what she wanted without guidance, rules, or limits), this person may feel neglected. If, on the other hand, parents were strict, critical, and constricted a child's ability to take the initiative or make decisions, he may suffer from feeling rejected or not good enough.

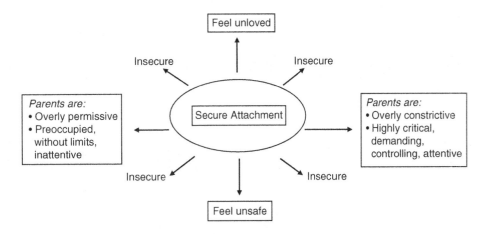

If a person felt unsafe growing up—environment and people were unpredictable, threatening, or abusive—then she may feel anxious inside. (It is assumed that she also would not feel loved enough.) This coupled with permissive parents or those with no respect for rules, agreements, or boundaries, may lead her to feel betrayed. If feeling unsafe was coupled with strict, constrictive, or overly critical parents he may feel constantly threatened or endangered.

Each of these elements are on a continuum, meaning that there are varying degrees of feeling unloved, unsafe, unattended to (overly permissive), or overly constricted. For example, someone may feel somewhat unloved to completely unloved; somewhat unattended to, completely neglected, or abandoned; somewhat criticized to feeling others are completely overbearing and controlling; and feeling somewhat unsafe to being in a life-threatening emotionally, physically, and/or sexually abusive relationship or environment. The initial experiences of feeling loved or unloved, safe or unsafe, unattended to or constricted can create patterns of thoughts, feelings, and behaviors to try to cope, avoid pain, and function in the world. Unfortunately, people can get stuck in patterns and end up replicating the very same patterns in relationship after relationship.

MILITARY FAMILY

Some people join the military in order to be part of a better family than the one they were born into. This is one way to form new relationship patterns—by having new positive experiences. There might have been hope that the military would be the caring, supportive, predictable, and safe family that they desired. If this dream is shattered by MST, it can serve to strengthen childhood perceptions (reinforce the original neural networks) and associated beliefs about being unloved and feeling unsafe. If, on the other hand, someone had a supportive childhood (secure attachment) and then MST occurs, the experience can shake that foundation and form new associations of fear. However, it is possible that those with a secure foundation fare better than those with an insecure foundation. In other words, although attachment style and *experiential holograms* are discussed as enduring styles contributing to repeating patterns, they are also able to change with new experiences that either confirm (strengthen) or disconfirm (weaken) the pattern.

Where Are You Along the Continuum?

Circle the number to the right of each question that corresponds to the scale below (from 0 = Not at all to 10 = Very much). Pick a number that best describes you feelings.

0___1___2___3___4___5___6___7___8___9___10

Not at all   Somewhat   Very much

1. How *unloved* did you feel as a child? 0 1 2 3 4 5 6 7 8 9 10
2. How *unsafe* did you feel as a child? 0 1 2 3 4 5 6 7 8 9 10
3. How much did you feel criticized, constricted, or controlled as a child? 0 1 2 3 4 5 6 7 8 9 10
4. How much did you feel your parents did not attend to you/were permissive as a child? 0 1 2 3 4 5 6 7 8 9 10
5. How *unloved* do you feel now? 0 1 2 3 4 5 6 7 8 9 10
6. How *unsafe* do you feel now? 0 1 2 3 4 5 6 7 8 9 10
7. How much do you feel criticized, constricted, or controlled now? 0 1 2 3 4 5 6 7 8 9 10
8. How much do you feel *you or others* do not attend to you/neglect you now? 0 1 2 3 4 5 6 7 8 9 10

Place your scores in the boxes below.

Degree You Felt	As a Child (Items 1–4)	Now as an Adult (Items 5–8)
Unloved		
Unsafe		
Criticized/constricted		
Inattentive/permissive		

Map your scores: Find where the number would be on each axis that corresponds with the score that you put in the chart above and put an X on the line. First plot the scores from childhood and connect the four Xs, then do the same for adulthood.

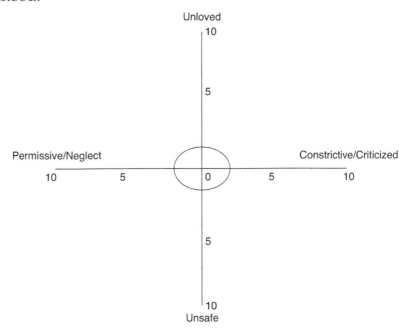

The inner circle represents "secure" attachment. Is there a difference between how you felt as a child versus now? Do your circles match with any of the following patterns?

1. Lopsided toward the upper left   → This may be Neglect
2. Lopsided toward the upper right   → This may be Rejection
3. Lopsided toward the lower left   → This may be Betrayal
4. Lopsided toward the lower right   → This may be Endangerment
5. High scores in all four quadrants   → This may also be Endangerment

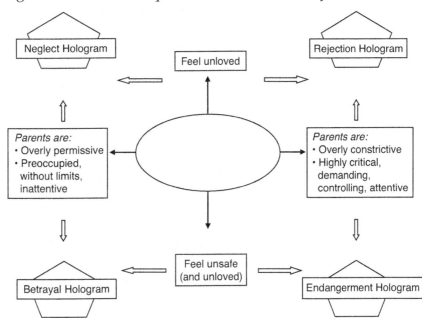

Elements That May Influence the Formation of Various Experiential Holograms

Experiential holograms can be activated by actual events as well as by memories, fantasies, and dreams. Because the brain reacts to thoughts in a similar way as to actual experience, a memory of a painful experience can trigger the neural network of associated thoughts, feelings, and behaviors. Emotional trauma such as neglect, rejection, and betrayal is often not seen or acknowledged by others or even by the person who experiences it. People may have to pretend or act as if their type of trauma or violation never occurred in order to protect themselves from further—or worse—pain. Because of this response, it is common to ignore, deny, or shut oneself off from one's true feelings. Responses to emotional traumas usually make perfect sense, given the experiences of deep hurt by someone once trusted and loved, and given what one had to do to survive. These types of trauma are tricky because, first of all, they may not be obvious traumas; secondly, they are usually perpetrated by family members whom the child loves and wants to please; and, thirdly, the child will invariably feel it is his or her fault or that somehow he or she is unworthy, wrong, confused, or not good enough. By taking on self-blame, the child is able to preserve the belief that the family is good and right, thereby doing whatever it takes to maintain a connection or relationship with them, even if they are the ones who perpetrated the trauma.

Unlike perpetrators of sexual assault, parents and family members may or may not be aware that they perpetrated emotional trauma. They are typically so caught up in their own issues, reacting to their own holograms and unmet needs, that they don't fully realize the effects of their own behavior (some are aware and some are not).

Most likely, you had a hologram formed prior to sexual trauma in the military and that hologram affected how the MST affected you. In addition, depending on the hologram, it may have played a role in making you more vulnerable to the sexual trauma (i.e., you had ways of interacting with the world that your perpetrator took advantage of). Again, this is NOT blaming you! But rather it acknowledges the manipulation of the perpetrator.

An example: Lucy was the only child of neglectful parents. Her parents divorced when she was 4 years old and Lucy recalls spending time alone or with babysitters. Lucy remembers that she often felt lonely. As an adult, she reached out to others for connection, but tended to choose people who may initially respond to her caring gestures but who did not reciprocate them. She stated that she stayed in these unfulfilling relationships because she valued loyalty and honored the ties of friendship and family. She believed that if she was attentive and caring they would feel loved and would reciprocate. Thus, she used the strategy of "being attentive" to try to secure relationships. When this was not reciprocated, she assumed it was somehow because of a deficiency in her. Therefore, each event of being neglected or ignored reinforced her perception that she was unlovable.

Lucy joined the military with the desire to be part of a new family. She worked hard and was proud of her service. When a male Marine asked her for a date, Lucy readily accepted. She did not know she was being set up for a sexual assault. This experience confirmed her worst fears and she felt used, unimportant, and left all alone. She engaged in avoidance behaviors such as withdrawal and "stuffing her feelings" by overeating. She neglected herself and her health, thus replicating the painful feeling of being neglected on a daily basis. This dynamic can be mapped as the following:

(1) Lucy feels lonely. → (2) She reaches out to family and friends (who are similar to her neglectful parents). → (3) They don't follow through. → (4) She feels she is unwanted and unloved. → (5) She tries harder to be attentive and caring. → (6) She is hurt and neglected. (7) She withdraws and overeats to avoid her feelings. → (8) She feels lonely.

Lucy has an *experiential hologram* of "neglect" with strategies to compensate for her feelings (reaching out to others) and strategies to avoid her feelings (withdrawing and overeating). Lucy came to believe that she was neglected because others didn't like her and she was simply unlovable. Lucy believed this because it was a conclusion based on her experience. The problem with this conclusion is that it is based on only part of the story. It is missing *context*. With further exploration, Lucy disclosed that her parents were 19 years old when they had her. Her parents married because it was the "right thing to do" although they were overwhelmed and unable to stay together. When Lucy, now an adult in her thirties, thought about the context of her parents' age, she understood her past in a new way. She understood that she was neglected because her parents were inadequate and unable to raise a child—not because *she* was unlovable! She also saw that the Marine had an agenda and she was a pawn in his plan—not that *she* was flawed. Reevaluating an *experiential hologram* and considering context is a process called *reprocessing*. Reprocessing will be discussed in future chapters. But first, let's examine various types of emotional traumas. See if any of these resonate or ring true for you.

TYPES OF EMOTIONAL TRAUMAS OR "CORE VIOLATIONS"

There are several types of emotional traumas or core violations that can be the driving force for people's holograms. Some examples are neglect, rejection, betrayal, invalidation, and endangerment. You'll notice these are not events such as "rape," "abuse," or "an accident." Events are certainly a source of trauma, but what specifically about the event made it traumatic? When we discuss an event of sexual trauma, what about it remains emotionally haunting and deeply upsetting? Is it because you felt your life was endangered, or was it that you felt betrayed by a trusted friend or fellow service member? The same event can mean different things to different people. The following are brief descriptions of four common *core violations*: Neglect, Disapproval/Rejection, Betrayal, and Endangerment.

Neglect Trauma

The trauma of neglect is probably the most common type of trauma and yet it is the most difficult to "prove" since it is the trauma of not doing something. This may take many forms such as not being protected from harm; not being attended to, listened to, believed, or understood; not being nurtured or loved; and not being taken care of. This may be overt or subtle and yet the results are terribly painful. People suffering from neglect may feel unworthy, forgotten, and unimportant. In fact, the trauma of neglect can be so dangerous that infants who are not held and given enough human physical contact, even if they are given food, can die. This is called "failure to thrive." Those who survive with neglect may have developed strategies to attempt to get their needs met; typically this means being very attentive to other people's needs, hoping that they will attend to them in return. But those with neglect violations tend to be givers attracting takers who never return the attention. People with neglect will give and give until they feel drained and resentful, and have unconsciously neglected their own needs, including time, money, and energy, while they were waiting for, but not receiving, love and appreciation. Are you a chronic giver?

Disapproval/Rejection Trauma

Feeling rejected is deeply painful, as it is the trauma of being told you are inadequate, not good enough, wrong, and unwanted. It is different from neglect. Where others could simply be preoccupied (and unable to attend to your needs), with rejection there is a deliberate act of not wanting or approving of you. This may be typical of a critical parent who focuses on wanting perfection. People with this violation tend to try hard to please others and achieve perfection. They believe that if they are good enough, then maybe they will be accepted and loved. This is of course an illusion, as they already are good enough but unconsciously have become their own worst critic and have learned to reject themselves.

Betrayal Trauma

Sexual trauma may include a deep sense of betrayal, or betrayal trauma. First introduced as a distinct theory by Jennifer Freyd, betrayal trauma occurs when people and/or institutions that we need, depend upon, and trust end up threatening or harming us (Freyd, 1996). Betrayal trauma can include childhood emotional, physical, or sexual abuse; mistreatment by members of institutions, such as religious, military, or educational; or any other violation by someone once trusted. It can also include the trauma of infidelity in romantic relationships or betrayal in friendships or other close relationships. This trauma may occur as a primary trauma (i.e., perpetrated by someone who was trusted) or it may occur as a secondary trauma, such as the violation of not being supported or believed by someone who was trusted (e.g., family member, good friend, or other military member).

Betrayal trauma is distinct from simple betrayal. With betrayal trauma, there is a shattering of a fundamental bond of trust. Those who suffer from this violation may feel they are unable to connect with others or allow themselves to have trusting relationships again. Because of a deep sense of loneliness and isolation, it is not uncommon that they attempt to trust someone but get into a relationship too quickly and suddenly feel betrayed again. People blame themselves and feel they can't trust others, but, worst of all, they feel they can't trust themselves or their own judgment.

Endangerment Trauma

This type of trauma happens when people have to live or work in an unhealthy, unpredictable, and abusive environment. Examples are living in a home with an abusive alcoholic, working under an abusive boss, or being in a relationship where you are the victim of domestic violence. Every day is unpredictable—"Will it be safe? Will there be an explosion?" People with this trauma are in a constant state of fear. They are also very alert and attentive to ward off potential danger. Some common phrases to describe this is "walking on eggshells," or "waiting for the other shoe to drop." Even when out of imminent danger, people with this trauma continue to expect bad outcomes and may even provoke a fight or explosion for relief (i.e., since it is bound to happen, let's get it over with). People with this hologram never feel safe. In addition, people with this hologram may report that they have all of the other holograms as well. This makes sense because someone who is abusing another person can be both critical and inattentive, in addition to betraying the person's trust. However, "endangerment" would be the overarching hologram and the other types of violations would occur in the context of endangerment. There are many types of characteristic coping responses such as wanting to be in control, or wanting/needing someone else (or something else such as an addiction) to be in control, avoiding relationships, or being hypersexual and having multiple relationships—and at the core of all of these responses is a desire to "feel safe" and decrease feelings of being unsafe (i.e., unsafe in relationships—physically, emotionally, and sexually).

There may be other types of violations such as feeling invalidated. This type of trauma occurs when perceptions of reality and aspects of oneself are invalidated and discounted. Imagine looking up at the sky and saying, "What a beautiful blue sky," and someone looks at you strangely and says, "What are you talking about; it's purple!" You would most likely look at the sky again and wonder what happened. Psychologist Solomon Asch conducted a number of social psychology experiments examining social conformity. He found that despite an obvious correct answer, some people were influenced to change their answer from correct to incorrect when a group of people confidently gave incorrect answers. But most people felt uncomfortable and stressed when their perceptions did not match those of others (see Asch, 1956). Social conformity can be a powerful influence on people's thoughts. Now imagine a child whose parents tell her that her feelings or thoughts are not right, not true, and don't matter. How about when she discloses that she had a sexual experience with an adult family member and her parents don't believe her, blame her, and invalidate her experience? This type of trauma may cause confusion, self-doubt, and a fundamental disconnection with trusting one's own perceptions of reality. It can also cause rage and frustration when people feel others do not take them seriously or validate their feelings. If invalidation is coupled with feeling unsafe, such as not being believed and continuing to be put in danger, then it may be "Betrayal" or "Endangerment" depending on where it falls on the continuum. If the invalidation is not associated with fears of safety but is associated with feeling criticized (e.g., the person is made to feel "stupid" or wrong), then it could be Rejection. If the invalidation is dismissing and ignoring, then it could be associated with Neglect.

Do any of these resonate as a core issue for you? Circle all that apply.

Four Clusters of Common Core Violations			
Neglect	Rejected/ Disapproval	Betrayal	Endangerment
Forgotten	Criticized	Others disloyal/ unfaithful	Threatened with danger
Ignored	Belittled	Manipulated	Intimidated
Deprived	Judged	Deceived	Trapped
Abandoned	Shamed	Promises broken	Surrounded by chaotic environment
Dismissed	Invalidated	Others untrustworthy	Physically/sexually abused

An example: Marty is a 42-year-old man who says that he feels lonely and angry a lot of the time. He grew up with parents who were "busy drinking and fighting." When Marty told his mother an older cousin touched his genitals, his mother laughed and told him to stop making a fuss over nothing. Marty felt stupid and ashamed for mentioning it. Marty left home as soon as he could and joined the U.S. Army after graduating from high school. Through the years, he has always wanted to have a good relationship with someone special, but says he has had terrible luck, always ending up with "losers and users" who take advantage of him.

One evening, Marty went to a bar near his base with a couple of his friends. His friends started talking to a few women and Marty felt bored. He took his beer and went outside to smoke. Two other Army men were outside smoking. They joked a bit and then invited Marty to join them to get something to eat. He thought that was "cool" so he agreed.

Although the guys were friendly at the bar, when they got in their car they started acting differently. They drove off quickly and hit Marty in the face. Once parked, Marty did his best to get away, but they overpowered him, hit him multiple times, and forced themselves on him. He passed out. When he woke up, they were back at the bar and they pushed him out of the car. Marty was furious. He was angry with "those bastards" and he was angry with his "stupid friends," but most of all he was angry with himself. How could he have been so stupid? How could he have trusted those jerks? He vowed he would never be used again. He vowed that nobody would take advantage of him and that he would "fight back" and seek revenge when he felt wronged.

Over the years, Marty has had problems with friends and coworkers, acting out in sometimes inappropriate ways—yelling in the workplace, "telling off" bosses—when he felt frustrated. He has a history of lawsuits alleging discrimination with several former employers. He has also had a number of romantic relationships that were combative, resulting in him perpetrating domestic violence. Marty prides himself on being a loyal and true friend, but when others disappoint him, he feels angry and that he is stupid and being used yet another time. Marty has few friends because he is sure that others just want something from him. Marty often flies off the handle when he is frustrated by interactions in which he feels duped, lied to, or that someone is taking advantage of him.

Marty's core violation is feeling "betrayed" or used by others that he trusted. His history of feeling betrayed is accompanied by a deep sense of feeling stupid, ashamed, and powerless. After feeling used, he compensates by pushing back—which ends up intensifying his feelings of alienation and loneliness.

What Is Marty's Experiential Hologram?

What is his core violation? How does he feel about himself and others? What does he do to compensate (to protect himself)? What does he do to avoid his feelings? What is he motivated to do in future relationships?

His *core violation* is: Betrayal and fear of being taken advantage of

His **beliefs about himself and others** are: "I am stupid and powerless and others will try to take advantage me"

His **compensating strategies** are: Fighting back and "making them pay"

His **avoidance strategies** are: Withdrawing, avoiding social contact

His **residual negative emotions** are: Loneliness, sadness, and anger

His **acquired motivation** is: To secure loyal relationships where "things are equal"

	Common Holographic Patterns	
Core Violation	**Personal Beliefs**	**Compensating Strategies**
Neglected	■ I'm ignored, dismissed, uncared for ■ I'm unwanted/I don't matter	■ Be wanted, funny, helpful, sexy, useful, caring to others
Rejected	■ I'm not good enough ■ I make mistakes	■ Be perfect, worry about details, have high self-standards
Betrayal	■ I'm stupid and gullible ■ Others are not trustworthy	■ Be wary/don't trust, but be loyal and trusting when I have a friend
Endangerment	■ My life is out of control ■ I fear for my safety	■ Be in control, safe, submissive to avoid conflict or upset

WHY YOU MAKE PERFECT SENSE

By looking into *experiential holograms*, you can begin to put together the pieces of your life—from core violations to compensating strategies—and how they shape the ways you may think, feel, and act. The hologram can help you understand why your particular trauma-based symptoms are actually coping mechanisms developed to protect you and help you survive, despite your circumstances. Given what has happened, you can see that you and all of your responses make perfect sense. In other words, do not blame yourself for having a certain pattern, but rather look for the ways that explain how your behavior developed for a good reason. Consider the context of your upbringing and all that you have experienced. If you think about it, you are rather brilliant for coming up with all of these strategies to cope! One group participant said, "This is amazing because I am the one pushing people away, making them confirm my own hologram, and then I get to prove to myself that I am right!"

WHAT IS *YOUR* HOLOGRAM?

Now that you have learned that we have holograms and characteristic coping styles, it is time to consider what your hologram is. We have defined *experiential holograms* as a pattern of thoughts, feelings, and behaviors that repeat themselves in relationships with others. The best way to figure out your hologram is to think about your relationships. What kinds of people are you attracted to or do you tend to become involved with? What draws you into these relationships? How do you feel once you are involved? What disappoints you most in relationships? How do you feel when the relationship ends? Answers to these questions will give you clues to your patterns.

Typically, these start in childhood and replay themselves in adulthood. They are most clearly seen in romantic relationships, but can play out in any or all relationships.

Writing Exercise

This exercise is adapted from *Journey to Your Heart* (Katz, 2006b). Take a moment and think about your close relationships (romantic partners, close friends, or coworkers). What kinds of people do you attract or tend to become involved with? What disappoints you most in relationships? How do you feel when the relationship ends? Using these instructions, complete the grid below.

1. In the first column, make a list of the people with whom you have been in an emotionally significant or long-term relationship.

2. In the second column, write a few adjectives about what qualities you liked about this person, or what attracted you to this person. *Alternate version*: Write a list of adjectives (personality qualities) that you would like in a person that you date.

3. In the third column, write the things you didn't like or that disappointed you about these people. *Alternate version:* Write what you dislike most in people that you would choose to date.

4. In the fourth column, write down the feelings you had at the end or shortly after your relationship ended. How did you end up feeling with this person? Even if you are still friends with the person, how did you or do you feel in these romantic, friendship, or business relationships? *Alternate version:* Write some of your feelings/concerns about getting into a long-term relationship or write some of the reasons why you are currently not in a relationship.

Below is an example of a completed grid. Can you see a pattern in this example?

1. Relationships	2. What Attracted Me	3. What Disappointed Me	4. How I Felt
Joe	*Intelligent, confident*	*Know-it-all, bossy, demanding*	*Disrespected, lonely*
Harry	*Independent, active*	*Too busy, non-committal, self-centered*	*Excluded, hurt, resentful*
John	*Athletic, intelligent*	*Self-centered, dishonest*	*Disrespected, lonely*
Sally	*Successful, confident*	*Controlling, dishonest*	*Lonely, invisible*

Now you try it for yourself. Follow the instructions above.

1. Relationships	2. What Attracted Me	3. What Disappointed Me	4. How I Felt

Look at your list. Circle words that are similar across relationships. Do you see any similarities across various people? How about in the feelings you had at the end of these relationships? Do you see a pattern? Next, complete the following sentences, inserting a summary of your answers from columns 2, 3, and 4 into the respective spaces.

Example

A. I am attracted to people who are: *confident, active, intelligent, and successful.*

B. These people turn out to be: *demanding, controlling, bossy, dishonest, and self-centered.*

C. At the end of these relationships I feel: *lonely, disrespected, invisible, and resentful.*

A. I am attracted to people who are _____

B. These people turn out to be _____

C. At the end of these relationships I feel _____

Now look back at your childhood. Can you think of a time when you felt similar emotions to the ones you wrote in the last question (C)? Was this feeling similar to how you felt with a parent or caretaker? Was it similar to what you observed in your parents' relationship? What do you think contributed to your feeling this way? Do you see any similarities with how you felt in the military? How were you treated?

Example

This is the story of my life. I felt this way as a child, as both parents were always so busy. I spent a lot of time alone or with a babysitter. When I tried to say how I felt, they just minimized my feelings and did what they wanted. Now I can see that I lived in a pattern of Neglect. I see how I felt emotionally neglected in almost all of my relationships. I am always focusing on making sure others feel okay, hoping they would appreciate and love me. But instead I feel drained, resentful, and empty inside. Funny, I also felt this way in the military. I tried SO hard to please my command. I would have done anything. But when my MST happened, I was treated like I was nothing . . .nobody cared. I was just ignored like I was dirt under the carpet. I never felt so lonely and empty inside before.

Use this space to process your thoughts and feelings.

_____

_____

_____

_____

_____

_____

_____

_____

_____

_____

_____

_____

_____

_____

_____

_____

_____

_____

_____

_____

_____

_____

_____

_____

_____

_____

_____

_____

_____

_____

_____

_____

Thinking about what you wrote, is there a theme across different relationships? How do you approach others? What do you most desire with others? What do you experience with others?

_____

_____

_____

_____

Shifting Relationship Patterns

This exercise is designed to shift negative patterns from your childhood. Most people enable certain patterns in their lives by either treating themselves or allowing others to treat them in certain ways. Instead of continuing the patterns based on what your parents did or did not give you, you can now become the healing parent for yourself. Answer the following questions:

1. **Write a few adjectives describing: What didn't get fulfilled for you as a child? Or, what happened to you that you are angry or resentful about?** (For example, "I didn't get acceptance, respect for my body, nurturing, guidance, protection, and encouragement," "I was rejected and discounted.")

_____

_____

2. **Name a situation where you still are not getting the above items in your adult life.**

_____

_____

_____

3. **How are you continuing these patterns in your life? How are you treating yourself or allowing others to treat you the same way?** (For example, how do you not accept yourself? How do you not respect your body? How do you let others mistreat you?)

_____

_____

_____

4. **Are you ready to commit to ending these patterns in your life? Are you ready to state that nobody is allowed to dishonor you again, including yourself?**

_____

_____

If you are not sure what your hologram is at this point, don't worry; this is a process of self-discovery. Maybe there are two or three themes that you noticed. Or maybe there is too much emotion right now to have an objective perspective. This is all part of the process. (For more information about *experiential holograms* and details about the specific components, see Katz, 2005). If you need to process your feelings, be sure to talk to someone about how you feel. Also, remember that images, memories, thoughts, and feelings may surface during this time. Allow them to bubble up to the surface and just let them be . . . notice what comes up for you. It may be a clue into your unconscious mind. Just notice your feelings without having to change, fix, stop, or alter your experience.

CONSIDERING MST

Now that you have explored patterns in your relationships, let's consider your MST experience. What do you think was most upsetting about it? Was it a sense of betrayal by those you trusted; fear for your safety; feeling neglected, dismissed, or ignored; feeling rejected; a sense of injustice; self-blame or shame; or maybe feeling isolated and completely alone? Do any of these fit for you? If so, which ones, and are they similar to your *experiential hologram*?

Common Core Violations of MST (Circle all that apply)

Betrayal	Shame	Neglect	Rejection
Injustice	Self-blame	Abandonmend	Endangerment

CHAPTER 7 SUMMARY POINTS

- Early experiences with a primary caregiver must be "good enough" for a child to feel loved and safe in order to develop an internal working model of trust. The inner working model influences a general expectation of how others will act, and, thus, also influences the individual's behavior.

- Secure attachment is a combination of elements: feeling loved enough, safe enough, trusting that a caretaker will hold boundaries and rules to protect you, and having enough freedom and trust in yourself and the world to go out and explore—knowing there is a safety net ready to protect and care for you.

- Four common emotional traumas are Neglect, Rejection, Betrayal, and Endangerment. These occur on a continuum of severity from mild to extreme.

- You make perfect sense! Your patterns developed for a reason—based on your experiences. How else would a person with your experiences think and feel?

■ Now that you are aware that you developed these patterns, you have a choice. Just because you experienced this in the past does not mean you have to continue living in this pattern in the future!

If you are emotionally upset . . .

If this process is activating your emotions and you are feeling stressed or overwhelmed, remember to take a few deep breaths and exhale completely. Also, smelling something such as lavender or vanilla (soap, candle, or aromatherapy oil) will give you immediate relief from emotional distress and improve your mood! Remember to take care of yourself when you are going through emotional work—rest, drink water, and remind yourself that you are healing!

Guilt, Self-Blame, and Shame

8

with Jane Hammerslough

Tell the truth and shame the devil.
—*Francois Rabelais*

- *Opening exercises: Exploring power*
  (Day 1: Game of power, Day 2: Guess the leader)
- *Closing exercises: Exploring power*
  (Day 1: Power postures, Day 2: Walking like a tiger)

THE DRAIN OF SHAME, SELF-BLAME, AND GUILT

At the root of every *experiential hologram* is a belief that somehow you are not good enough, loved enough, or safe enough. The reason for these beliefs, ironically, is not typically attributed to one's caretaker or to one's perpetrator, but instead is personalized and attributed to oneself.

Children will inevitably believe abuse or maltreatment is their fault or somehow because of a flaw or deficiency inside of them. Similarly, in adulthood, after trauma such as MST, it is likely that people harbor some level of self-blame, shame, and guilt. This occurs because people invariably wonder, "Why did this event happen to me?" And without a logical explanation, it is common to think, "Well, if it happened to me, then it must be because of me...." This is an attempt to make sense of something that does not make sense. Therefore, self-blame is a strategy—not necessarily a logical conclusion, but rather a way to make a random senseless event less random and senseless. It is also a strategy to help you feel that somehow you had control. This can occur by thinking maybe you could have or should have done something differently, as if you could have changed the course of events. Maybe if you knew what was going to happen, you wouldn't have gone on the date, agreed to a drink, stayed late at work, or said "Hi." Some people obsess over a thought for many years: If only they did or didn't do something, then this wouldn't have happened. But at the time you didn't know what was going to happen. You acted in ways that you thought made sense. Even if you think, "I should have known" or "I had a funny feeling," these thoughts are still an attempt to control (as if you had control) a situation that was completely out of your control. Why do people do this? Simply because they wish it hadn't happened. It is a form of resistance— "No, no, no! This should not have happened; I should have stopped it; I should have done something. . . ." If you find yourself relating to this, then you may be struggling with accepting what is. Just like the color of a blue pen, this will not change no matter how much you want it to. It happened because *someone else* wanted it to happen—regardless of what you could have done. This is an important piece of the picture: *The past happened the way it did because other people were involved and made it happen that way.*

A particularly distressing side effect of shame, self-blame, and guilt is that it is emotionally draining and exhausting—undermining your sense of self-worth and competency. It affects how you may see yourself and how you may interact with others. While sometimes self-blame and shame may be helpful, often it is not productive at all, contributing to a sense of isolation, inferiority, and other unhelpful emotions. For many survivors of sexual trauma in the military, these emotions may be especially intense, tied up with not only self-esteem but one's career and the honor of being in the service. In this chapter, we will explore how and why you may experience these emotions and learn ways of challenging them.

Shame

Shame, like many feelings, can be either productive or potentially destructive. In general, shame is a feeling of being embarrassed or humiliated about one's behavior in a specific situation. This might include feeling ashamed at the way you handled a situation—or were treated in a situation. If feelings of shame lead to remorse and the desire to correct a bad situation to make sure it doesn't happen again in the future, the emotion can be productive. In this way, shame and remorse may be tools for learning and self-improvement. For example, feeling ashamed about failing a test might motivate a student to study harder for the next one.

However, if shame is how someone feels about one's character or is used to put someone down, it can become destructive or even abusive. Being repeatedly told that one is unworthy—in both overt and subtle ways—can lead to feelings of depression, humiliation, and/or despair. For example, after sexual trauma, someone may muster the courage to disclose what has happened, expecting empathy, understanding, and help. However, not everyone knows how to react and they may make unhelpful comments such as wondering why you put yourself in the situation. This is not only unhelpful, but may provoke feelings of shame.

Blaming a survivor so he or she feels shame and/or takes responsibility for another's actions is a form of continued abuse. This behavior puts the focus of blame and shame on the person who was abused, diverting it from the person doing the abusing. For example, an abuser might announce, "She made me hit her." Did the person who was hit actually ask to be hit? Of course not! But the suggestion is that the person who was hit was to blame—and ought to feel ashamed—because she brought the abuse upon herself. (Blame is a common ploy of abusers.)

There are many reasons why people blame the victim—it may preserve a sense that the world is still safe, predictable, and under control. People might think, "Well, if it happened to him or her because he or she did something to bring it on, then the rest of us remain safe and it won't happen to me." This is naïve thinking. These things happen at alarmingly high rates, with higher rates in the military compared to civilian populations. The odds are it can happen to anyone regardless of what one was wearing, doing, or drinking and regardless of whether one screamed, fought, or ran. Sexual trauma does not occur because of these things and it is a false belief to think it is the victim's fault. The fact is *it is the perpetrator's fault*!

Blaming the victim is not only manipulative, but it perpetuates feelings of shame—and prevents healing from things that happened that were not the victim's fault at all. It is important to be aware of the ways that a sense of shame is communicated by others as well as the unhelpful, inaccurate things that we may tell ourselves—that may get in our way of working through trauma.

> **Doubt is the brother of shame.**
> –Erik Erikson

Self-Blame

Self-blame is not always negative. Healthy self-blame, like remorse, is a way of taking appropriate responsibility for one's actions. It requires reflecting on what happened and how one's feelings, thoughts, actions, and words contributed to the situation. When appropriate, it can be helpful when examining one's own integrity, values, and behavior. This can also be a productive and positive learning tool.

However, too much self-blame is counterproductive. This typically occurs when someone takes full responsibility for a bad situation regardless of other peoples' actions. In other words, while others might have contributed to or even caused a situation, one person takes all the responsibility and all the blame is attributed to the self.

Self-blame is common among adult sexual trauma survivors and, in particular, it is very common among children who grew up in situations where abuse occurred. People who endured chronic abuse, or lived in an environment of abuse, tend to blame themselves even when it was the perpetrator who did the action! Why does this happen? One reason some people do this is because it may be a continuation of the type of "shame and blame the victim" tactic as discussed in the previous section. Additionally, self-blame allows people who have been abused and feel powerless to have control over a situation that was out of their control. If they can blame themselves, then at least one thing in the world remains somewhat predictable and may be somewhat comforting. This is a desperate attempt to make sense of a situation that does not make sense. As already stated, people think, "If this abuse is happening to me then it must be about me, and therefore it is my fault!" This in itself is also part of the abuse.

TYPES OF SELF-BLAME

Two common types of self-blame include *behavioral* and *characterological*.

Behavioral Self-Blame

Behavioral self-blame involves the notion that blame is temporary and based on certain behaviors. It may include thoughts such as "I should have locked the door," "I shouldn't have got into his car," or "When I think about what happened I realize that my judgment may have been impaired at the time," and encompasses taking some responsibility for a situation occurring. When coupled with reflection and positive action, behavioral self-blame can enhance a sense of control in challenging circumstances, and may lead to changing behavior to alter outcomes in the future.

Characterological Self-Blame

Characterological self-blame implies a permanent and absolute state, and includes thoughts such as "I am a bad person," "I am worthless," and "Bad things always happen to me so I must deserve it," as opposed to the notion that sometimes good people may be involved in bad situations. Because it is narrow, inflexible, and negative, characterological self-blame is not productive for healing. Additionally, it focuses only on one person involved in the traumatic event, removing responsibility from the perpetrator and taking actions out of context.

Other characterological self-blaming thoughts might include "What is it about me that would cause people to do these bad things to me?" or "It was all my fault that this happened, I should have known better. . . ." This can become a recurring monologue of self-blame and resulting shame that is never resolved. Trauma survivors who characterize themselves as the cause of their traumatic incident fare less well than those who do not.

People who experience behavioral self-blame seem to fare better than those who experience characterological self-blame. Why do you think this is so?

_____

_____

_____

Did You Know . . . ?

Most survivors of sexual trauma have felt self-blame at one time or another. Taking a step back, putting the event into context, and viewing it from an observer vantage point—like viewing your life on a television screen—helps to create a narrative that includes the other people involved and details how the situation occurred. This can create a more complete picture of what happened and help lessen self-blame.

Putting Blame Where Blame Is Due

While an overwhelming number of trauma survivors experience shame or self-blame, it is very important to view the situation holistically and put blame where blame is due. While there are few absolutes, some things are clear: Victims of trauma were in the wrong place at the wrong time. Other people are usually involved, either actively or passively. The environment where the trauma occurred—from the values of others to the physical space—may also play a role in the event. It is important to examine each of these factors to gain greater understanding of what happened and assign blame in a more accurate fashion.

It is also important to note that many survivors blame themselves for their actions in a traumatic situation and fall into "could have, would have, and should have" thinking—to continue blaming themselves! This kind of thinking ignores the fact that the survivor may have done something right. It is helpful to try to examine the situation from a different vantage point and consider that the things he or she did—or didn't do—during an attack or other traumatic event that may have helped him or her (and possibly others) survive.

Meditation on Shame, Self-Blame, and Guilt

Nobody is going to give you power and nobody can take it away.
Nobody is going to give you self-esteem and nobody can take it away.
Nobody is going to give you security and nobody can take it away.
Nobody is going to give you peace and nobody can take it away.
These are things you already have, and only you can give them away.

GUILT

Guilt is a unique feeling. Unlike other feelings where there is a potentially productive quality, guilt really has little to none. Guilt is feeling bad about doing something that you believe you shouldn't have done—or *not* doing something that you believe you *should* have done. Unlike remorse, which can lead to productive learning and possibly taking action, guilt offers little opportunity for change. Instead, it simply feels bad, sitting in the bottom of one's stomach like a heavy stone. Carrying the heavy stone around doesn't do anyone any good and it just weighs heavily on the person carrying it.

A common way that survivors of trauma feel guilty is through statements that begin with "If only. . . ." For example: "If only I had stayed in the kitchen a few minutes longer, then I might not have run into the person who hurt me" or "If only I could have kept my big mouth shut, then none of this would have happened. . . ." As survivors work through issues of trauma, it is common to think about "If only . . ." scenarios, which inevitably will lead to regret and guilt. "If only I had turned right instead of left"—as if you had a crystal ball . . . as if you could have known what was going to happen. What can be done about it now? Nothing. It just sits there like a heavy stone.

Guilt and Manipulation

In the same way, if you feel, or have felt, obligated to please someone, then guilt is probably controlling your decisions. In this case, guilt may be a manipulative threat: If you don't do what someone else wants you to do, then you're a bad person or it will be your fault if something bad happens to that person. Of course, very few of us have that kind of control or power over someone else, yet we may feel guilty if we don't do what they wish.

When guilty feelings arise, it is important to consider the whole picture once again: What is the responsibility of the other person in this situation? Is someone making his or her emergency your emergency—expecting you to own and take care of his or her problems? How much do you really need to take on and how constructive is feeling guilty? Sometimes people try to cross the wires between love and manipulation, such as saying, "If you loved me (or were a good daughter, boyfriend, friend, etc.) then you would do this for me." Although it may be wonderful to help someone and certainly people want to help those they love, it is also important to consider the whole picture—by considering both your own needs as well as those of others. There are many points of view and multiple solutions to every situation, which means you don't have to feel cornered by threats of guilt. Communication skills on how to handle these types of situations will be reviewed in Chapter 11.

Guilt and Grief

Another way guilt occurs is when someone is grieving a loss. It is not uncommon that people feel guilty, as if they should have helped more, visited more, or somehow done something that could have changed the course of events. When people are grieving the loss of a loved one, they typically feel guilty as part of the grieving process, or coming terms with or acceptance of the loss. However, if people are not able to work through the grief, they may develop complicated grief and may get "stuck" feeling guilty. Guilt is a sign that the person has not completed his or her grief.

PERPETRATORS OF SEXUAL TRAUMA

As noted, sexual trauma occurs in many different forms and each one is a violation inflicted upon a victim by a perpetrator. Most acts of sexual trauma are premeditated or opportunistic. In other words, someone knows exactly what he or she is doing and either sets up a situation to make it happen or waits for an opportunity. This person chooses victims and situations in which it would be easy to get away with it, without getting caught. The most common weapon in sexual assault is not a gun or knife (which is the stereotype), but rather manipulation, trickery, and sometimes alcohol and drugs. This makes the assault easier for the perpetrator.

Sometimes perpetrators are strangers, but more often than not they are known to the victim in both civilian and military traumas. They may have planned the event and tricked, lied, or manipulated the victim into a situation where he or she could be taken advantage of. This adds to the confusion since victims and friends of the victims might blame them for getting themselves into the situation. They ask, "Why did that happen to you?" and victims also think, "Why did this happen to me?" instead of considering the rest of the story—that the perpetrator knew exactly what he (or she) was doing.

An example: Nellie was on her third date with Matt. She met Matt through a friend of hers. She had every indication that things were going well and he was a nice man. Therefore, when he invited her to dinner, she did not hesitate to go in his car for their date. However, when he forced himself on her, afterward people questioned her, saying, "Why did you go in his car?" She even thought that herself and felt guilty for putting herself in a vulnerable situation with him. But the reality is that she was responding to normal social cues, doing what most people do on dates. Why wouldn't she go in his car? If she knew what he was planning, she would have done something differently. But she didn't know. Matt seemed like a really nice guy and she trusted him. The fact is, Matt manipulated and lied to Nellie. He knew exactly what he was doing—perpetrators always know what they are doing. But Nellie still harbors self-blame.

This is a very common symptom of sexual trauma. You may also have been set up and lied to just like Nellie, and yet feel that somehow it was your fault. You blame yourself for doing things: "Why did I help him, stay late after work, trust her, go for a walk?" and so on. You may also blame yourself for not doing things: "Why didn't I scream, fight, or report the incident?"

To answer the latter concerns: You already know that "freezing" is a stress response. It is a normal part of sexual trauma to not scream or fight. You had to survive. In fact, research suggests that fighting can make some perpetrators more violent and more dangerous. Sometimes freezing is the most adaptive response there is. Also, these things are unexpected, so while the perpetrator knew what he was going to do, you had no idea—and were taken off guard. This element of surprise, shock, and confusion also leads to a freeze response.

You also know that you were in the military, in a context where it may not have been safe to report the incident. Would you have been believed? Would you have been blamed? Would something worse happen to you in retaliation? There are probably very good reasons if you did not "scream, fight, or report the incident," including simply being afraid.

ADDRESSING SHAME, SELF-BLAME, AND GUILT

When we consider bad things that have occurred in our lives, many people tend to ignore the context of the event, and personalize traumatic events: "Why did this happen to me?" "What is it about me that made this happen?" This is an interesting conversation, because it only focuses on a small part of the picture and completely ignores the question, "Why did this other person do this awful act? What is wrong with him (or her) that he would do such a thing?!" An important aspect of understanding sexual trauma is putting it into its proper context. What other circumstances were involved? Who were the other players in the scene? What was the environment like?

It is important to understand that sexual predators target people. Even if you agreed to go with a perpetrator, agreed to have a drink, and thought you were romantically interested, none of these things give someone the right to violate you or force themselves on you. Sexual trauma, by definition, is not a mutually consented act. Therefore, regardless of what you think you did or did not do, sexual trauma cannot be your fault. Maybe you didn't protect yourself or prevent the situation—but that is not the cause of the trauma. The cause is the action of someone else. You would not have needed to protect yourself if someone else wasn't attacking you. Considering context will help you see the roles of other people who were involved. If you were set up and tricked, context will clarify this part of the picture. If others blamed you as a form of abuse, then context will help reveal people's true intentions and agendas. For example, consider this: "What do they gain out of blaming you?"

CREATING A "RESPONSIBILITY PIE"

Is it really all your fault? Before assuming 100% of the responsibility for an interaction or situation, let's make a realistic appraisal about the whole situation. Who was directly and indirectly involved? How much did each person contribute to the situation? How much did you, the survivor, contribute to the event occurring? How much responsibility can be attributed to chance or unforeseen circumstances? If you add the total of all of these factors, it should equal 100% responsibility for a situation.

To create a *responsibility pie*, assign a percentage of responsibility to the people, places, and other things involved in the situation, including you, so that it adds up to 100%. Draw a circle and divide the pie into wedges, assigning a percent of responsibility to each slice.

For example, a person who experienced having her wallet stolen might attribute 80% of the responsibility for the incident happening to the perpetrator, 10% to chance, and 10% to her handbag having a loose latch. The person who picked her wallet out of her purse might have chosen her specifically to rob, but part of the incident occurring had to do with bad luck and timing. Her *responsibility pie* might look like this: *80% perpetrator, 10% chance, 10% loose latch*.

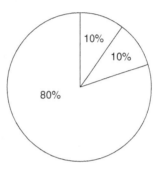

Now, think about a traumatic event that occurred to you. How much can be attributed to the perpetrator, chance, military environment, bystanders (friends and coworkers), and yourself? Is there anyone or anything else to share the blame? What would your *responsibility pie* look like?

__%: _____ __%: _____ __%: _____ __%: _____

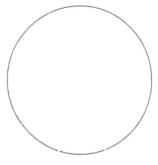

Now, let's reconsider the pie chart you just created. Maybe you feel guilty because of the mere fact that it happened. But in actuality, there is no way you could make someone behave in the manner that he or she did. Someone else crossed the line with you, regardless of whether you were on a date, drunk, naked, or felt obligated/threatened to participate. By definition, sexual trauma occurred because someone else violated you. Let's put blame where blame is due. Let's reconsider these pie charts. If in the example of the stolen wallet her purse was wide open, no latch, and she was at her friend's house, do you think the fact that her purse didn't latch means her friend has a right to steal her wallet? Hopefully not! The purse is not the cause of the theft; it was the thief. Maybe a locked bag would have prevented the event from having been completed (or then again, maybe not). But certainly the thief had the intention, plan, and did the action to carry out the crime. The thief was a thief regardless of the condition of the purse. Does it make sense to blame the purse for the violation? Maybe the thief would have found a way to take it anyway, latched or not latched. The purse is a purse whether latched up or not and cannot be the cause of its own theft! It is the thief who is the one who intentionally committed the crime. Would you agree that it is impossible to blame a purse for its own theft? Similarly, you are the purse and a perpetrator committed a theft of a sexual nature against you. Does that change anything on your responsibility pie?

If so, draw your new responsibility pie below:

__%: _____ __%: _____ __%: _____ __%: _____

How do you feel after drawing your new pie chart? Does it change the way you think about responsibility and blame? _____

_____

UNDERSTANDING CONTEXT AND MULTIPLE POINTS OF VIEW

As the one who has experienced sexual trauma, you are well aware of your thoughts, feelings, and what you wanted in the situation (e.g., get away, survive, protect yourself, etc.). But you were not the only person in the situation. There was at least one other person, the perpetrator, and maybe others involved before or after the event. Each person had their own agenda and perspective on the event. Maybe the perpetrator was making sure he could get away with it; maybe others were protecting their own safety or just didn't want to get involved. The same story can be told in many different ways from the viewpoint of each person involved.

There is a common saying that in any interaction, there are always three truths: yours, mine, and the truth!

The following is a hypothetical example to explain the concept of "multiple truths." A father is concentrating on preparing his taxes. He is upset and frustrated because he realizes that not only is he missing documentation, but it appears that he will have to pay a substantial amount this year.

He is in the middle of adding a long list of numbers when his 4-year-old son runs through the room, disrupting the father's concentration and blowing some of his papers onto the floor. Suddenly the father yells, "Get out of here, you lousy kid!" His son is jarred and frightened by his angry father. Since his father tends to have a sharp temper, the child experiences this event as a potential threat of losing love (of the parent), losing security (will the parent still provide?), as well as losing self-esteem ("I'm lousy"). The father's communication was angry, disapproving, and rejecting with a specific blame on the child as being the cause of his anger.

The child experiences the words spoken by the parent as the truth, and concludes that his father is angry with him because he is "no good." After all, the father is yelling at the child and did call him a "lousy kid." Therefore, it is a perfectly logical conclusion for him to assume his father's anger is his fault. The child's conclusion is not faulty or wrong, it is merely too narrow and limited. In order to have a different perception of the event, the child would need to have the ability to see a bigger context for the parent's response. This is unlikely, because (1) it may be beyond the developmental capacity of a young child to assume that there even is a different context for his father's anger, (2) the child was not given any indication that his father's anger was a displacement from his own frustration with the taxes, and (3) even if the child was told his father was really upset about the taxes and not him, he still *experienced* his father's anger directed toward him and this experience would be difficult to deny.

However, viewing the same scene as an objective observer, you can see a very different story. The objective observer may perceive that the father's anger and harsh words had nothing at all to do with the child! The father's reaction was as an indication of his own frustration and emotional problems. Both the child's and observer's conclusions are logical and accurate although they are contradictory. In other words, there are "multiple truths" to this event. From the child's perspective, there may be no doubt that what is perceived is the truth, while from the observer's perspective a different truth is obvious.

The "personal truth" as part of an *experiential hologram* is a perception of truth given a particular vantage point, usually formed from the perspective of the one who experiences a trauma. It is formed from a personal experience. However, it is a limited perception as it does not take into account the perspectives of other people involved in an interaction, or that of an objective observer. This construct is called "personal," as it defines a narrow personal perception.

In this treatment, participants are encouraged to see multiple explanations of events, thus broadening their viewpoints. It is important to note that each of the viewpoints is valid and no attempts are made to disconfirm a perception or label it as faulty or wrong. As in the above example, how else could the child interpret his father's words? The child did not have access to a broader context. Acknowledging that a trauma survivor's interpretation does make sense given limited available information is experienced as validating and compassionate. Acknowledging that one's interpretation was right seems to ease the transition from a limited personal truth to accepting a broader concept of truth about a situation.

Multiple Truths

Imagine Jill was shown a red square. Jill's experience would be the evidence to convince her that indeed it was a red square. However, Bill was shown a blue rectangle. His experience was the evidence to convince him, beyond a shadow of a doubt, that what he saw was indeed a blue rectangle. Now what if Jill and Bill saw the same object—how could that be? Was it a red square or a blue rectangle? The answer is that it is both red AND blue. They are just different sides of the same rectangular-shaped box with blue sides on the long ends and red sides on the square ends. Each side was perceived accurately, but neither Jill nor Bill saw the whole box. Each saw a truth, but it was not the *whole* truth.

This helps explain how you can perceive your experience as self-evidently true, but at the same time it may not be the whole truth. The "whole truth" is another way of considering context.

When you review the events of your life as an objective observer, think about what happened as if it happened to someone else or as if you are a scientist or reporter. Consider everyone involved. What were the thoughts, motives, and agendas of the perpetrator and others?

Writting exercise. **Consider what happened in your experience of MST or other trauma.**

1. **What happened? (brief description of the core violation)**

_____

_____

_____

2. **Who else was part of the events or circumstances?**

_____

_____

3. **What do you think each person named above was thinking from his or her own perspective? What were his or her motivation, agenda, and self-serving emotional needs?**

Person A. _____

_____

_____

Person B. _____

_____

_____

Person C. _____

_____

_____

Now what do you think about what happened? Someone else was involved with his or her own agenda that had nothing to do with you! It happened to you, but it could have been someone else with the same outcome. *How does it feel to consider letting others be responsible for their behaviors? Remember, like in the example of the purse, an open purse does not create theft; only a thief can create a theft!*

You can do this exercise again, thinking about your childhood. What were the agendas and motives of the people in your family? Can you see it from their perspective? Were they preoccupied, stressed, or focused on their own needs? How does this explain your experience in a new way?

Person A. _____

_____

_____

Person B. _____

_____

_____

RELEASING SHAME, SELF-BLAME, AND GUILT

The following are five ways to release shame, self-blame, and guilt:

1. *Boost self-esteem.* First, remember that no matter what has happened, what you did or didn't do, you are still a good person. The fact that you're reading this book and working on yourself means you care about yourself and you care enough to learn and grow. This is a wonderful quality! There are many things about you that you can be proud of.

2. *Make a list of ten positive qualities about yourself.* This list can include nice things you could say about yourself, positive ways you act with other people, things you are good at doing, and other ways that you are awesome! Alternatively, go around the room and let the group members say something positive about each participant.

3. *Practice self-forgiveness.* Are you ready to forgive *yourself*? Remember, you did the best you could in the situation at the time. Of course, if you knew what you know now, you might have done something differently. But you didn't know it at the time. So, from the

perspective of what you knew at the time, can you forgive yourself? Can you consider that it wasn't *all* your fault? Can you tell yourself that you are still a good person regardless of what happened?

4. *Practice good self-care.* Instead of beating yourself up, it's time to build yourself up. When was the last time you indulged in some good self-care? Taking a bubble bath, getting a manicure/pedicure, walking in nature, going to a fresh juice bar, taking a yoga class, or doing something healthy just, a for you? Also, a little positive self-talk also goes a long way. Can you think of something kind, loving, and encouraging that you could say to yourself?

_____

5. *Complete grief.* If guilt persists, then it is important to assess whether there is still incomplete grief about a loss. If this is so, resolving the guilt means resolving the grief. (The next chapter addresses losses and grief.) But if these feelings persist, then it may be helpful to write about these feelings or seek the assistance from a mental health provider.

Writing exercise: **A letter to your younger self.** Take a few moments and imagine you could visit your younger self. What would you like to say to him or her? What does he or she need to hear from you? What can you give your younger self that would provide him or her comfort, love, and safety? What else does your younger self need to hear—that it wasn't his or her fault? Take a few moments to write a letter to your younger self. *Note:* This can be ANY age younger than you are now—from childhood, to the young self in the military, to yourself as an adult in an abusive relationship, or any other younger self that could benefit from a letter from your current-age self. You may even want to write more than one, such as one to your childhood self and one to a younger self in adulthood.

_____

_____

_____

_____

_____

_____

_____

_____

CHAPTER 8 SUMMARY POINTS

■ Blame is a common response to trauma—others blame the victim to preserve their own best interests, and victims also blame themselves. Why? Because it happened to them! The logic of this conclusion is very faulty and completely ignores blaming the perpetrator.

■ Behavioral self-blame is blaming specific behaviors such as "I should have done this . . ." and it can help people feel they have a sense of control. However, characterological self-blame, or blaming oneself with thoughts such as "I am bad, stupid, and worthless," is unproductive and can interfere with healing.

■ Putting blame where blame is due is a process of examining an event from an objective viewpoint. Who is really responsible for this? Making a *responsibility pie* helps people realize that it is impossible for sexual trauma or abuse to be "all your fault." First of all, the perpetrator was the one who crossed the line and only the perpetrator can be responsible for what happened, regardless of your behavior, what you said, or what you wore.

■ Multiple viewpoints help people see that there are many sides to the same story. This broadens the understanding of the event or series of events so people can see it in its context. Who else was involved and what was his or her agenda?

■ Sexual assaults and abuse typically happen by perpetrators who premeditate and plan their attacks using trickery, lies, and manipulation. They know exactly what they did.

■ Finally, remember the positive things about yourself, and practice self-forgiveness and good self-care!

Losses and Grief

9

> Give sorrow words; the grief that does not speak whispers the
> o'er-fraught heart and bids it break.
> —*William Shakespeare*

- *Opening exercises: Community*
  (Day 1: Rain, Day 2: Cupid)
- *Closing exercises: Release and mindful awareness*
  (Day 1: Release, Day 2: Mindful awareness)

LOSS AND GRIEF

The Many Facets of Loss

Loss associated with MST and trauma may take many forms. These may be actual losses or the loss of certain potentials of a future that never happened. Losses may include health issues, loss of a career, loss of relationships, an unborn child, and/orability or desire to have children. Losses may also include abstract things such as time, innocence, or changing your worldview. Although these losses may be painful to think about, the flip side is also true. With every alteration or change in your life there may be losses as well as gains (which we will consider at the end of this chapter).

Defining Your Losses

What are some things you feel you have lost as a result of MST?

_____

_____

_____

No doubt your life changed as a result of MST. Many of the outcomes were certainly not what you had expected to have happen in your life and you have had to endure lifelong consequences. What could have happened in your life if you never experienced MST is impossible to know—you may think it would have been "better," but you don't know for sure. For example, Betty was sexually assaulted in the U.S. Army in the 1960s and it resulted in a pregnancy. This was an automatic discharge and Betty regretted that her military career was cut short and ruined. She never "got over" this pain. However, when asked what might have happened if she stayed in the military, she realized she would more than likely have been sent to Vietnam during the war. For the first time she considered that possibly the MST saved her life. She felt she would have been "torn to pieces" in the war. This does not make the MST okay, but it did help her consider a possible benefit to something that is otherwise awful.

In the process of working through feelings about trauma, people may first experience anger and resentment about the incident. And while anger may be justified, not processing angry feelings and maintaining the anger or resentment may be a way of defending against actually feeling the grief associated with the trauma. Grieving related to a trauma is a powerful emotional process of acknowledging feelings.

Experiencing loss and grieving may include physical, emotional, social, and spiritual responses. Some common physical reactions include feeling very tired or restless, having trouble sleeping, and feeling an ache or emptiness that doesn't go away. Along with sadness, some common emotional responses include feeling anxious or lonely. Reactions to other people may include avoiding people and places or overreacting to others. Finally, spiritual responses may include repeated questions, wondering how something so bad could have happened.

> **No one ever told me that grief felt so like fear.**
> —*C.S. Lewis*

As with the mourning process that occurs with the death of a friend or loved one, traumatic grief is a natural process of working through what we may have lost as a result of a trauma. Grieving is essential for coming to terms with and processing the trauma and resultant losses. When we are able to experience, express, and resolve grief over our losses, we can move forward in a new way.

WHAT IS GRIEF?

Grief is the process of coming to terms with what is. It is the process that occurs before people come to acceptance. It can be a painful experience involving many different feelings. In previous chapters, we have discussed anger, guilt, shame, and blame, and how they may be linked to traumatic events. Working to identify how you feel in other ways, and considering how those feelings are connected to a sense of loss, can help you begin the process of grief.

How many of these emotions do you experience? Which are your strongest feelings?

Afraid

You may feel afraid, without really knowing why, or fear that you will never feel "normal" again.

Alone

Loss can be lonely, especially when it is due to a traumatic event. It may feel as if nobody else could ever understand your loss or pain, and it may feel isolating.

Betrayed

You may believe that you were unfairly treated by someone—or many people—whom you trusted, and who was involved in your loss. It can be hard to shake that sense of betrayal when you are grieving.

Bitter

Loss feels unfair, and you may feel disappointed and cheated out of something that you once had. You may wonder why you, of all people, experienced this loss.

Confused

It may be hard to make sense of your loss, and you may have a hard time focusing or making decisions in one or more areas of your life.

Depressed

Your mood and energy may be low, and you feel that there is little relief or end for those feelings. You may feel unmotivated to do activities or be around other people.

Sad

The sorrow associated with your loss may be hard to shake; it may feel as if you will never be truly happy or laugh again.

Disconnected

You may feel detached from others. Although you can be physically next to people, emotionally you may feel distant and alone. You may also feel disconnected from the traumatic experience itself, where it may feel as if it happened to someone else, or seems unreal.

Helpless

Because you were not able to prevent the traumatic event from occurring, you may feel powerless or incapable in other areas of your life.

Hopeless

Your sense of loss may begin to overwhelm hope in the future, and you may begin to feel that nothing will ever change.

Numb

You may not be able to feel much of anything, and may not care about anything either.

Overwhelmed

It may be hard to stop thinking about your loss or worrying about what you might lose next, to the point that you feel like escaping through substance abuse or self-destructive behavior.

Vulnerable

You may feel exposed, without protection, to whatever may happen next.

Yearning

Your loss may feel like a constant emptiness, a void that cannot be filled.

Do you have any of these feelings? How about any other feelings that are not listed here? These are all normal, typical responses to trauma and loss. What are some ways that you can address the strongest feeling? What are things that you once did that might help you feel less alone, betrayed, or sad? Giving yourself a chance to have a break from your feelings of grief—for example, allowing yourself 2 hours of watching a comedy, taking a walk in a beautiful place, or being with a trusted friend—where you will simply focus on experiencing the present time may help. It is also normal and typical to allow these feelings to come and go as you work through the grief. Just because you feel moments of joy, laughter, or connection does not negate your grief. In fact, toggling between the positive and negative emotions may help you process and tolerate them. This means going back and forth, even if it means starting with only a few moments of feeling okay during the day.

Incomplete or unresolved loss can result in ongoing grief as well as feelings of guilt or shame. People can get stuck in these feelings—and stop the grieving process. By not acknowledging losses or finding validation for your feelings, it is not uncommon to feel alone, or to blame yourself or others for the trauma, no matter how unrealistic or untrue that really is. It is important to recognize the complexity of the losses experienced as a result of a traumatic event. This will help you release the associated feelings that have been attached to the memories of the event.

The event happened. It was wrong and unfair and certainly something that you did not want. Getting stuck on blame or shame does not help you process the grief. Furthermore, getting stuck on thoughts such as "Why did it happen?" or "Why did it happen to me?" is a sure-fire way to feel frustrated and upset. There may be questions that will never be answered. But as discussed in previous chapters, in many events, specifically sexual trauma, there were others involved. Sometimes, even though it happened to you, it may have had nothing to do with you. (Remember putting blame where blame is due?)

HUMANS LOVE MEANING

Humans seem to love to make things mean something. We go about our lives making meaning: "This means this and that means that!" "If she said this, then that means she is untrustworthy." "If he said that, that means he is a jerk." "If she was my friend, she would do this." "And if he loved me, he would know to do that." We are constantly judging others, coming up with conclusions, and assuming how others should behave even when we don't have all of the information. In fact, when we don't have all the facts, there is a tendency to make up answers to explain events. "How come she complimented her instead of me? Does that mean she likes her better? Or maybe it means this or that. . . ." But the truth is that maybe it doesn't mean any of that at all! We jump to conclusions to try to make sense of things that don't make sense. So why did the MST happen? Why did it happen to you? We don't know why; most likely just because you were there—and nothing else.

THE WAY LIFE SHOULD BE

Each of us grows up with a sense of how things "should be," from expectations of morality and fairness to how we may have envisioned ourselves living as adults. We want to believe certain things about the world and ourselves, and experiencing trauma can shake those beliefs. Trauma and its accompanying sense of loss may result in a terrible sense of disappointment and failure. We may continue to grieve because we do not want to let go of our old hopes or beliefs.

Imagine that each of us has a "book of the way life should be" in the attic of our minds—a big old dusty book that sits upon a pedestal. It has a heavy leather-bound cover and thousands of tissue paper-thin pages. Imagine on page 372 it says that when you turn 21 your life should be like this. On page 564, it says that at age 30 you should do this, and on page 1280 it says that at age 52 you should do that. The book has all of the rules, expectations, and ideas that you have about how the world should be, how you should be, and how others around you should be. That is what the book says. So what happens when something happens that is not in the book? "Hey, that is NOT supposed to happen!" And that is absolutely correct, because according to your book it was not supposed to happen. The problem is that not everyone has the same book in their heads. In fact, most likely everyone has a slightly different version of the book, so that means you can't expect other people to literally be on the same page!

What happens when you expect and want things to be a certain way and they don't happen that way? How do you feel? Do you get angry or disappointed at others or life for not adhering to your book? In fact, it is almost a guarantee that you will feel upset.

But life is bigger than what is in "your book."
Although you are part of life, you cannot control life.

We have a tendency to blur our perceptions, thoughts, feelings, and desires with life itself instead of realizing we can generate or create thoughts and feelings independent of what has occurred or is occurring in life. An example of this is a very famous painting of a pipe by René Magritte titled *Ceci n'est pas une pipe*, which translates from French to "here is not a pipe." How does that make sense? A very realistic painting of a pipe is titled *Here is Not a Pipe*? So what is it?

Well, it is a painting of course! Certainly a painting is not a pipe (you cannot smoke a painting). In other words, a painting of a pipe, no matter how realistic, is still not an actual pipe; it is a representation. The problem is that our minds respond to and treat representations as if they are real. Remember the lemon exercise in Chapter 3? You had a physical response to an image of a lemon. If you think it, your body responds as if it is real. Just like responding to a painting and saying, "Oh, that's a pipe!" even though you know very well that it is a painting. The point is, just because something is in your head about how things should be does not necessarily predict the reality of how things are.

Sexual trauma should not have happened. There are probably other things in your life that also should not have happened. And as distressing as these events are, they did happen and it does not have to mean anything more than that: an event that happened. It also does not have to define you or your future. Don't confuse yourself with MST. You are not MST, you just experienced it. And when you work through the grief associated with MST, you will loosen the attachment and fusion with it. It will begin to float back to your past, where it belongs.

> If you suppress grief too much, it can well redouble.
> —*Moliere*

Delayed Grief

Without even being aware of what we are doing at the time, we may postpone reacting to the loss until later—sometimes years later—and it may feel overwhelming. Many things, including stress, can trigger the grief we may feel years after an event. This grief may include having intense feelings of distress, restlessness, or hopelessness, being extremely tearful or sad, or other feelings. A small loss in the present time may be the trigger to bring up old unresolved losses. As discussed before, this is like plugging in a string of holiday lights. Once the string is plugged in, other lights along the string light up, so one loss brings up past feelings of loss.

No matter how delayed grief may be, it is important to recognize that the feelings of loss are valid and real, and may remain with us until we acknowledge those losses. The impact of experiencing trauma and the ways we become aware of our feelings are different for each person. Years later, those feelings may be more intense than ever. It is also important to remember that these responses are normal, and that survivors are not alone. Working with mental health professionals and other survivors can be extremely helpful in working through the grieving process.

> There is no trauma without grief; there is no grief without trauma.
> —*Therese A. Rando*

Complicated and Disenfranchised Grief

Resolving grief is important for healing. However, when trauma-related grief is complicated by other feelings—feeling as if one is "losing control or will go crazy" if he or she thinks about the event, feeling "weak" or at fault in not preventing the trauma, or feeling that the trauma was somehow "deserved"—it may continue without resolution. Many traumatic events are unexpected, sudden, and violent. These qualities may contribute to complicating grief.

While there are parallels to other types of mourning, the grief of trauma is frequently "disenfranchised." Disenfranchised grief is the mourning that is not openly recognized, publicly acknowledged, or socially supported by society, family, or friends in the same way that traditional losses such as the death of an adult family member. Disenfranchised grief may result from a rape or assault experience; a miscarriage or giving a child up for adoption; sexual, spousal, or childhood abuse; discrimination; and other traumas. Survivors who have experienced events that are overlooked, dismissed, or avoided by others and who do not feel validated in their losses may have a prolonged sense of sadness and grief.

Did You Know . . .

Kenneth J. Doka, in his book *Disenfranchised Grief: Recognizing Hidden Sorrow* (1989), describes disinfranchised grief as loss that is not openly acknowledged or socially sanctioned. He asserts that people who experience disenfranchised grief often do not receive the rights of the grieving role, including sympathy, support, and/or compensation from others. When others do not recognize the pain of loss, it may lead the person experiencing grief to feel guilt, shame, and isolation.

WORKING THROUGH GRIEF

The grieving process involves acknowledgment and acceptance of loss. Telling your story about the things that you may have lost, whether physical, emotional, and spiritual or simply the loss of potential, is the first step in this process. Expressing feelings can help release the pain, and accepting the losses takes the energy out of them, like letting the air out of a balloon.

In processing grief related to trauma, it is important to be patient with yourself. Though other people may have gone through similar experiences and seem "fine," your own mourning is unique, as is your own healing. Knowing that you will eventually feel better and that you are not alone in feeling loss and traumatic grief is important.

Elizabeth Kübler-Ross (1997) identified five stages of grief that occur when people are terminally ill or face the loss of a loved one. These include denial, anger, bargaining, depression, and acceptance. However, later research showed that these stages do not necessarily occur in this sequence. Some people may skip one stage or another, or cycle through all of them several times. Some people can get "stuck" at one stage and may have difficulty moving on. If one stage pops out and resonates strongly for you, it may give you some insight on where to focus your efforts for healing.

1. *Denial and isolation*: This is oftentimes considered the first stage of grief, characterized by feeling shocked, tearful, and unable to comprehend the event, and by isolation from others. In this stage, people say they cannot believe what just happened.

2. *Anger*: In this stage, people feel angry, outraged, and resentful. They may be hostile to others (angry at the world). They may also develop physical symptoms such as headaches or stomachaches and increased pain. Thoughts at this stage focus on injustice and revenge.

3. *Bargaining*: The third stage is characterized by being reluctant to let go, so people may try to bargain and set up private deals and prayers such as "I promise I'll go to church every week if you change this outcome." These are attempts to change something that cannot be

changed. People may hold onto blame, either of themselves or others. "If only" thinking and blame keeps them stuck in this stage of grief.

4. *Depression*: The fourth stage is acknowledging and mourning the loss by feeling sad, defeated, and realizing that the loss really happened. People may be tearful, numb, and have intrusive thoughts reminding them about the loss.

5. *Acceptance*: The final stage is acceptance or surrendering to what is. People realize what happened and now it is time to readjust to reality. This means coming to the here and now and choosing to live.

Weeping may endureth for the night, but joy cometh in the morning.
—*Psalms, 30:5*

TRAUMATIC GROWTH

It is what it is; we cannot change the past. It may have been terribly wrong, unfair, and tragic . . . but it happened. Okay. When you are ready, and only when you are ready, allow the past to be in the past. But before we completely let it all go, it is worth considering the other side of losing something, and that is finding something. Although this might seem counterintuitive, going through intense experiences always leaves a hidden trail of something positive. Like golden dust brushed up from the dirt, at first all that can be seen is dirt. But in the dirt are precious particles that you might not otherwise have ever found if you had not traveled your path and kicked up the dirt.

What do you think you might have gained from the experience that caused you so much pain and loss? How have you grown and changed in positive ways such as developing character, values, passion, determination, compassion, or a broader perspective, or are maybe stronger in ways that you might not have ever anticipated? Through grieving what we have lost, we sometimes discover what we now have.

_____

_____

_____

_____

Imagine that each of us, moving through the world, is like a honeybee flying and stopping at flowers. Some flowers may have more pollen and nectar than others and some may be sweeter than others. Some, in fact, may offer little more than sharp thorns or slippery stems. Still, as the honeybee stops along the way, it picks up bits of pollen—like the golden dust—to carry back to its hive.

All experiences in our lives are a bit like that "golden dust." Whether positive or negative, they become part of what we carry though life. They contribute to who we are and what we become. They may lead to other circumstances, situations, events, and feelings, changing our outlook and sometimes opening our minds and opening our hearts. All along the way, we pick up something meaningful. Even the most traumatic experiences contribute something to who we are.

For example, the bits of "golden dust" that we pick up along the way through our experiences of trauma and healing may include a greater acceptance of many things, from self-acceptance and our own limitations to the limitations of other people. We may find "gold" in a greater ability to keep our strength and resolve, with the knowledge that we can make it through some very dark times and emerge into the light. We may find greater self-awareness and self-reliance. At the same time, we may also be learning that we can begin to trust and accept help from others.

Living through trauma and recovery deepens our understanding of both pain and joy, which enables us to become more compassionate. The experience of healing may lessen our need and desire for control and enhance our sense of humbleness and gratitude for survival and for the good things in our lives. It may help us gain insight and knowledge into ourselves, and into whole other worlds outside of ourselves.

Perhaps most of all, "traumatic growth" means gathering that "golden dust" of our experiences into a sense of heightened awareness of the intricacy and richness of our lives and ourselves—both in the past and in the future.

Trauma is an experience. It may be a terrifying or life-threatening experience, but nonetheless it is an experience. You have many experiences in life—some pleasant, some not so much. But these are events that happened. You learn from each experience and sometimes what may have been the worst experience gives you the greatest opportunity. Can you think of an example? How about being so fed up with a job that you decide to quit, only to meet someone who opens up a whole new set of opportunities for you? Maybe you would never have had those opportunities if you stayed in that job.

MINING GOLDEN NUGGETS IN THE DIRT

Name one to three benefits or things you've learned as a result of going through trauma.

_____

_____

_____

What have you learned (about yourself, others, humanity)?

_____

_____

_____

_____

How has living through all of your experiences inspired you to do something positive in the future?

_____

_____

_____

_____

Listening to Your Inner Wisdom

A large part of healing is paying attention to your intuitive and helpful "inner wisdom"—listening to the wisdom from deep within yourself that you know is right, but don't always hear or heed. If there is still a message of fear or sadness—perhaps from a younger self—that needs to be heard, it is helpful to "go back" and speak to that message, from the vantage of being older and wiser. Reassuring messages such as "You're going to be okay," "I'm here to tell you that you are doing the best you can," "You will survive, and I will be here to help," and "I will take care of you" are all powerful statements that can help you heal.

One participant said, "_A broken heart is an open heart . . . what happened to me in the military broke my heart. Now I am learning new things about appreciation, gratitude, and wanting to help others who have been through what I have been through._"

Being Present

Living in the present—"being here now"—means understanding and accepting what was and what is. We cannot "un-ring the bell" of our experiences, but we can live with our current reality with purpose and meaning. This can occur each day by speaking and living our truths. By doing this now, we are not sucked into or stuck in the past. Best of all, we can feel hopeful about the future when the past no longer holds us in its grasp.

Our "being-ness" in the present is like water: No matter what happens to it, water is still water. If you heat it, it becomes a gas. If you freeze it, it solidifies into ice. But regardless of what occurs to that water, it is still made up of two parts hydrogen and one part oxygen. It is always H_2O. Likewise, you are always you! No matter what has happened to you, your essence, or that special uniqueness that is you, is still you. Whether you are in a happy or sad mood, you are still you—that does not change. And you have the potential to be all emotions, have many different thoughts, and express yourself in numerous ways. You have had and will have many different experiences, meet many different people, and still you will always be you, learning and growing and experiencing life.

We are always our core selves, no matter what form we take. As we add the "golden dust" to our lives, we allow ourselves to grow and evolve. As we heal, we may grow and change, but fundamentally we are whole and undamaged, like water taking on new forms and shapes. We survive experiences and feelings, and we abide by our wholeness and our truths.

> **Our dreams must be stronger than our memories. We must be pulled by our dreams, rather than pushed by our memories.**
> —*Jesse Jackson*

Gratitude List

You've heard the saying "count your blessings." What does that mean? Everyone has things to be grateful for, and remembering *all the good that you do have* will help improve your mood and keep you from getting stuck on thinking about what you don't have.

What are you grateful for?

_____

_____

_____

_____

_____

_____

_____

_____

_____

_____

HEALING ATTACHMENT, HOLOGRAMS, AND THE BRAIN

It takes an adult brain to shape a child's brain. The child cannot regulate his or her emotions alone; he or she needs an adult to do this for them. A child's brain has not developed these skills and needs to learn in order to develop. A mother mimics her child's emotions (including facial expression, reflecting the baby's emotions back to the baby). This is very validating for the child! Then the mother offers soothing messages such as "It's okay!" to help the child feel safe and regulate his or her emotions. Literally, we have neurons that mirror the neurons in others called *mirror neurons*. These light up and mirror (duplicate or simulate) in our own brains the feelings of others. "Empathy," thus, is neurological and deeply woven into our neurobiological and social functioning. When parents are chronically unable to meet their children's needs, or provide reassurance and security, the child tends to behave in ways that reflect an internalization of the parent's characteristic responses to them. If a dismissing mother, for example, responds to her infant's distress by ignoring or suppressing it, that infant may well develop an avoidant strategy for dealing with her own painful feelings—in other words, she will avoid or suppress them. The children of insecure parents "borrow" their parents' defenses, and thus the legacy of parental insecurity is often a parallel insecurity in the child (Fonagy et al., 1995). Attachment, internal working models, and experiential holograms are all ways of understanding patterns that were developed in childhood or after trauma that set in motion certain thoughts, feelings, and behaviors that replicate themselves in relationships.

The good news is that attachment and holograms can be healed as you as an adult heal. Because of neuroplasticity, or the ability for the brain to heal and form new connections, the neurobiology of attachment can actually improve and change. In a way, psychotherapy is a process of "re-parenting" the inner child who may have had less than ideal caretaking. John Bowlby (1988) asserts that psychotherapists can provide patients with a secure base from which to explore painful aspects of life, both past and present. These painful memories may be too difficult or perhaps impossible to think about and reconsider without a trusted companion to provide support, encouragement, sympathy, and, on occasion, guidance.

In addition, your current-aged adult self can also re-parent your own inner child. You know better than anyone what you needed as a child, teenager, and/or young adult and didn't get (i.e., your unmet needs), and you know better than anyone what would help you heal: feeling safe, loved, accepted, validated, and nurtured.

If you could go back in time as your current-aged adult self and see yourself as a child or in the military, what would you like to say? What would you like to do? Imagine that your younger self can receive this communication from you right now and really take it in. Imagine your brain mirroring these emotions, forming new neural pathways. Imagine that as you feel safety, love, and acceptance you are forming new, more secure attachments. Neurons related to old holographic patterns begin to detach, the connections becoming weaker while new, more healthy patterns become stronger.

Doing this healing work is like rewiring your brain. Imagine a wad of wires all interconnected with each other. You are an electrician rummaging through the wires, working on untwisting or detaching some connections and twisting together new connections. Every time an old circuit fires and does not connect because it has been interrupted, the impulse to fire that circuit weakens. Similarly, every time a new circuit fires and is reinforced with a positive charge, the impulse to fire the new circuit strengthens. This is the way to weaken old, unhealthy patterns and build new, more positive ones.

REPROCESSING

Now that you have defined your hologram, you know your core violation, have released anger and resentments toward your perpetrator with poetic justice, have come to radical acceptance of what is, and have explored putting blame where blame is due, you may be ready for "reprocessing" your hologram. Reprocessing is an imagery-based exercise where you, as your current-aged self, visit your younger-aged self (see Katz, 2005, for more details). (This can be ANY age self younger than your current age right now.) You've already considered the context of what happened and have written a letter to your younger self. Is there anything else you would like to tell her or him? Something you would like to do? Some people want to give their younger self a hug and let them know it wasn't their fault, they are good and worthy, and from now on they will be protected, listened to, and cared for. The idea is that you as your current-aged self, knowing what you know now, have an opportunity to right something from your past. Your current you can offer the caring, understanding, encouragement, or safety that your younger self didn't get. The idea is to give yourself what you didn't get as a child, young adult, or any other time in your past when you were hurt, neglected, betrayed, or mistreated.

A Few Questions to Assist You in Reprocessing

1. **What is your core violation (to the best of your ability)? Neglect, rejection, betrayal, trapped/endangerment, or invalidation?**

_____

2. **What was your unmet need (e.g., lack of attention, acceptance, loyalty, freedom, safety, or validation)?**

_____

3. **What do you know now about the situation in terms of context and putting blame where blame is due?**

---

4. **What would you like to tell your younger self? What does he or she need from you?**

In reprocessing people imagine revisiting their younger version of the self. From this observer viewpoint, people can imagine "stepping into" the scene as their current self and offering empathy and understanding to the younger version of the self.

For example, Sandra completed reprocessing of being gang-raped in the military. She said when she looked back on it, over 10 years later, she realized that she was "an innocent lamb attacked by wolves" and it wasn't her fault. She said she loved visiting her younger self and telling her it wasn't her fault, that she is safe now . . . she said she held her hand and said, "Don't worry; you're with me now."

In reprocessing, you remain you as your current-aged self and imagine visiting your younger self. This helps minimize fear and triggers because you are safe now and in this present moment.

When Edward learned about reprocessing, he was skeptical and hesitant. But afterward he was surprised that it "wasn't that bad!" He reported that he felt a tremendous relief, including feeling less ashamed and less blamed.

Exercise: Recalling Last Night's Dinner

The following exercise will help explain the difference between recalling an event *as if re-experiencing it* versus recalling an event *as if observing it*. When you re-experience an event it is as if it is happening to you right now. However, if you are observing it, you watch the event from afar. To understand recalling an event from the observer vantage point, try this exercise.

1. First identify what you had for dinner last night (or another recent meal).

2. Then take a *cleansing breath* to relax. Gently close your eyes and recall last night's dinner as you were *reliving the experience* of eating dinner. Imagine yourself taking a bite of the food. Make the image as vivid as you can . . . and then open your eyes.

3. Now, let's do the exercise again. But this time recall the event as if you are observing yourself eating dinner. Take a *cleansing breath* to relax. Gently close your eyes and recall last night's dinner as if you were *observing yourself* eating dinner. Imagine yourself taking a bite of the food. Make the image as vivid as you can . . . and then open your eyes.

What did you experience? What did you notice the first time? How about the second time? Which time did the food taste better? Which time did you notice things about the space around you and how you looked? Which time did you notice how you felt?

_____

_____

_____

If you found that recalling the event as if re-experiencing it had more emotions and you could taste and feel the food more, and if you found that observing the event you noticed how you looked and what was around you, then that is consistent with what others found when they did this exercise. McIsaac and Eich (2002, 2004) conducted studies examining how people recall memories and compared a field vantage point (as if reliving it) to an observer vantage point (as if observing it). Field vantage point was more emotional and experiential while observer vantage point gave the experience context. In reprocessing, we use the observer vantage point, so instead of imagining *being* your younger self, you imagine *observing* your younger self. The idea is to imagine your current-aged self having a conversation with your younger self.

DO NOT REVISIT AN IMAGE OF TRUAMA!

*Question: Why do we **not** revisit trauma in reprocessing?* First of all, reprocessing is not a desensitization procedure. It is not meant to trigger or traumatize you, but rather it is a gentle imagery exercise designed to help you connect with your younger self. This can be emotional but not frightening.

Question: How should I feel before doing this exercise? People may feel many things, but remember you are the one in control of your imagery. Think about what you want to say/do before you do the imagery, and you can stop at any time.

Preparation for Reprocessing

1. Think of an age of your younger self that you would like to visit. Where is he or she? What is he or she doing?

_____

_____

2. What would you *want to say* to your younger self? What do you think your younger self would like to *hear from you*? (e.g., "You're going to be

okay," "I'll take care of you," "It wasn't your fault," "You did the best you could," or "I love you!")

————————————————————————————

————————————————————————————

3. **What would you *want to do* for your younger self? What do you think your younger self would like *you to do*?** (e.g., go to a garden, keep her in your heart, give him a hug, or give her a special present).

————————————————————————————

————————————————————————————

Imagery exercise: (Note: This is a guided imagery exercise along a country road. *If a country road is a trigger for you, do not use this image.* Instead, use another image that is relaxing for you, such as walking along a beach, in a forest, or by a lake . . . do what is most comfortable for you!) This exercise works best if someone else reads it while you close your eyes and concentrate on the imagery. Take your time. Pause. And breathe . . . !

Start with two to three *signal breaths* (take a deep breath in through the nose, hold it at the top for a few seconds, and slowly exhale through the mouth). Feel yourself sitting in your chair, feet on the floor and back supported by the chair. Release any tension in the body—relaxing your shoulders and breathing. . . . Now imagine walking on a country road. The sky is clear and blue. Maybe there is a small white cloud in the distance. It is a warm, sunny day and you can feel the warmth of the sun on your skin. You can hear birds chirping in the trees. You are walking on a path lined with trees and flowers. The colors are vibrant and the air smells fresh and clean. Imagine walking on this beautiful day . . . allowing yourself to relax and take in this pleasant scene. Where are you on a scale of 1 to 10, where 10 is tense and 1 is very relaxed? See if you can continue to relax . . . breathing . . . bringing your level down one notch at a time. . . . Excellent. . . . Up ahead you see a grassy clearing; approach the clearing. You can stop here for a while if you would like to continue to relax—maybe you hear a nearby stream bubbling and birds chirping in the distance, or you just bask in the sun. Take in all of the beauty of this scene. And breathe. . . .

When you are ready, imagine seeing the home of your younger self in the distance. If you would like, approach the place knowing you are your current-aged self. You are safe and bring with you all the knowledge and wisdom you have gained up to this point of your life. Imagine going to the door, breathe . . . and when you are ready, imagine opening the door. . . .

You can see your younger self in the room. What is she doing? Would you like to approach her? What would you like to say to her? What does she want or need to hear from you? Spend a moment talking to your younger self. [pause] Do you want to do anything else? Does she need anything from you—a hug or a special gift? [pause] Spend a moment giving your younger self what she needs. [pause] Is there anything else you would like to say or do? Would you like to leave her in the room or take her somewhere else? [pause] Are you ready to go? When you are ready and feel complete . . . imagine returning to the grassy clearing with the nearby stream . . . and then walking back on the country road . . . noticing the trees and flowers. . . . Slowly bring your awareness back to the room, sitting in the chair, feeling your body supported by the chair. Wiggling your fingers and toes. . . . Slowly open your eyes, stretching and yawning. Take two to three *cleansing breaths*—deep breath in through the nose and out of the mouth with a sigh. Take a moment of silence.

How are you doing? What did you experience? Spend a few moments of silence to process your thoughts and feelings through writing.

_____

_____

_____

_____

_____

_____

_____

_____

_____

_____

_____

_____

_____

_____

_____

_____

_____

_____

_____

_____

_____

_____

_____

_____

_____

_____

_____

_____

_____

_____

_____

_____

CHAPTER 9 SUMMARY POINTS

- There are many emotions related to grief: fear, being alone, feeling betrayed, bitterness, confusion, depression, sadness, disconnection, helplessness, hopelessness, and feeling numb, overwhelmed, vulnerable, and/or empty.
- We try to make sense of things that often do not make sense. We try to create a story so that there are reasons to explain the unexplainable—but often these are inaccurate and lead to faulty conclusions such as self-blame. When things happen that violate our sense of how

the world is supposed to be, it can be devastating. However, the assumption that the world is supposed to be a certain way is in itself inaccurate.

- Grief that is unresolved from the past may activate in the current time. This may be "delayed grief."

- Kübler-Ross offers five stages of grief: denial, anger, bargaining, depression, and acceptance.

- Traumatic growth is finding the "golden nuggets in the dirt" or the good things that you may have learned as a result of going through trauma. The grieving process may help you identify that even the worst experiences teach us valuable lessons.

- Remember your gratitude list to help shift your mood in a positive direction.

- The neural connections in the brain can heal and change with new experiences. Your current-aged self can also assist in healing your younger self.

- Finally, reprocessing means going back to your younger-aged self and repairing the brain by letting your younger-aged self hear what he or she needs to hear.

Healthy Intimate Relationships

10

- *Opening exercises: Exploring balance*
  (Day 1: Balance, Day 2: Peruvian ball passing)
- *Closing exercises: Exploring balance and love imagery*
  (Day 1: Exploring balance, Day 2: Love imagery)

HEALTHY RELATIONSHIPS: A BALANCING ACT

This chapter starts with an exercise of standing on two feet and staying perfectly still. Is it possible? Next close your eyes and notice all the subtle movements that are required to stay balanced. Now try standing on one foot. As the seconds tick by, you probably notice that as you try to stay balanced on one foot, the rest of your body is constantly making tiny adjustments. In fact, if you try to stand perfectly still on one foot or even two, you will find it's impossible. Although you may not be consciously aware of exactly how you do it, your body adjusts and adapts naturally. Contrary to what we might think, balance is not obtained by staying perfectly still, but rather is achieved by shifting, changing, and staying flexible. Being in the moment and relinquishing control, allowing your body to move and adjust, is how we can actually achieve balance.

Similarly, relationships are a dynamic process. Successful relationships, particularly for people who have experienced trauma, are not about total control or staying perfectly still and avoiding all upset—but about staying flexible and open to possibility. It is impossible to have an authentic relationship without some upset sometimes, just as it is impossible to remain standing on one foot without wobbling a bit sometimes.

But the goal, both in foot-standing and in intimate relationships, is not to avoid upset, but is rather to allow for it and make adjustments to maintain balance. In relationships, there may be a blend of healthy boundaries, mutual respect, good communication, and caring. While total control may be an illusion, greater awareness—of what you bring to a relationship and what you hope to receive from it—is a good place to start to building better relationships. This chapter will explore various levels of intimate relationships, trust issues, and ways of staying balanced and healthy in relationships with others.

> Happiness is not a matter of intensity, but of balance, order, rhythm and harmony.
> —*Thomas Merton*

Did You Know . . .

Harville Hendrix, author of *Getting the Love You Want* (1988) and *Keeping the Love You Find* (1992), believes that each of us has an image—an "Imago"—of our earliest caregivers in our unconscious minds. This Imago is made up of both the positive and negative traits of mothers, fathers, and other people who were meaningful in early childhood. Hendrix believes that the Imago—including both positive and negative qualities, and needs that were met or unmet by those people—forms a "blueprint" of qualities we seek in a partner. How have your early experiences affected your choice in partners? How has this been positive? How has this been negative?

LEVELS OF LOVING RELATIONSHIPS

Just as there are stages of development and learning as a child grows, there are stages of learning intimacy that humans acquire as they develop. As people mature and grow, they tend to move through these developmental stages. However, people can get stuck at a certain stage of intimacy development, especially as a result of interpersonal trauma such as betrayal, broken trust, and hurt and pain caused by an intimate partner or family member. This section will examine each of three stages of intimate relationships. These stages apply to both heterosexual and same-sex relationships. Can you recognize your own relationships—or past relationships—in any of these?

> All love shifts and changes. I don't know if you can be
> wholeheartedly in love all the time.
> —*Julie Andrews*

Stage 1: Dependence

When we think of romance and love, it is part of our culture to imagine a beautiful princess rescued by a handsome prince, who by a magical kiss seals their future for a happily ever after. Similarly, people may dress up and go out to meet an interesting potential mate, hoping to be swept off their feet by the mate's declaration of attraction (and "love"). The hope is that a kiss or a night of passionate sex seals the relationship and true love will be forever. Media reinforces this fantasy with statements such as "It was love at first sight," and "I knew she was the one the minute I set eyes on her." Although logically this does not sound realistic, it still does influence people's thoughts, hopes, and behaviors—a wish that lingers in the subconscious mind.

Can you think of a song, movie, or fairy tale that perpetuates instant "true" love?

Stage 1 relationships are founded on these wishes—of complete fulfillment and happily-ever-after. Couples at this level are very dependent on each other, and hope that their partners will fulfill their emotional needs. This is not unlike the intimacy of an infant with its mother, cooing at each other and sharing a special bond, and also being completely reliant on the other person. At this stage, the sense of "we" is very powerful, to the point that each of the members of these couples cannot distinguish his or her own feelings from the partner's feelings—which doesn't leave much room for things such as differences of opinion! So when one person has a different opinion, makes a request, or desires to see his or her own family or friends the other person may become threatened. This may be expressed as anger, passive-aggressive actions, unreasonable demands, or clinging behavior. These behaviors in turn cause threat in the other person, usually escalating into a fight.

At this stage of a relationship, couples may be very passionate and extremely involved with each other. On the upside, Stage 1 relationships can be very exciting and romantic—at least for a while. On the downside, they can be emotionally draining, swinging between bliss and blame, love and hate, make up and break up. These relationships may be controlled by conditional requests or demands: "If you loved me, you would. . . ." Couples at this stage sometimes like to categorize themselves as "madly in love" and then turn around and fight just as passionately. While this may be exciting in the short term, ultimately, it may be too drama-filled to sustain itself.

The problem is that people lack communication skills and instead rely on assumptions. "If we are twin-flames, then we should think the same, want the same things, and should be one." One couple came into couple's therapy because they were fighting. When asked what sparked the fight, one person said, "I knew when she served me broccoli we were finished. I hate broccoli and she should have known it." He assumed that if they were really soulmates they would have the same preferences and be able to read each other's minds.

Stage 1 relationships are the most attentive, most romantic relationships. They start fast and intense. Because of the adrenalin rush and intense experience of euphoria, they can be addictive and people can hop from one relationship to another with very little time without a partner. These relationships feel great in the beginning, especially if someone has a neglect hologram. Why? Because they are so attentive and exciting. For a moment, the emptiness inside is gone. However, because there is no foundation to the relationship it cannot sustain itself. After the relationship crumbles, the feeling of being empty inside returns and the idea of attentive romantic intimacy becomes enticing, regardless of the potential consequences. Without much thought, you may dive right into another Stage 1 relationship, once again destined for a train-wreck disaster. Why do these relationships end up so miserable?

If someone has a neglect hologram where he or she feels empty inside, the desire is to find someone to fill the hole. However, the chosen partner is also empty inside, also wanting to be filled up. Is it possible to fill someone up? Not really; the blissful state is only a temporary distraction from each person's own unresolved pain. When the pain creeps back, the partners blame each other. For example, one may think, "You are the cause of my misery! I was happy before—why did YOU take it away? If only you would do what I say, then we'll be happy again. It's your fault we are miserable." This is the basis of domestic violence where the blame escalates into actions and one person tries to control and dominate his or her partner.

But the blame is misdirected. The misery happened long before the relationship. The misery is deep unresolved pain, maybe from childhood, previous trauma, emotional neglect, and poor attachment with one's parents. Maybe both partners are trying to heal their neglect holograms by being in an attentive relationship. But it is impossible to avoid the underlying pain and think the bliss will last forever. It is a fantasy that "they saw each other from across the room and knew it was love!" It is a fantasy, a childhood wish of perfect union and perfect love. The truth is, love requires more than attraction and the desire for bliss. It is impossible to sustain the fantasy without an authentic friendship and communication skills. Luckily, these are the tasks of a Stage 2 relationship.

Can you describe or think of an example of a Stage 1 relationship? Can you think of an example on a TV show/media or something you have observed in your life?

What do you think is the biggest challenge in these relationships?

How do Stage 1 couples manage issues such as the desire to be right?

> Harville Hendrix had an incredible revelation! He ran down the stairs to tell his wife: "Honey I know the secret to the success of our marriage!" She waited for the insight. He said with glee, "We are happy because we realize that I am not you and you are not me!"

Stage 2: Independence

Relationships in Stage 2 might be considered the middle stage, or adolescence, of relationship development. Couples at this stage are independent individuals with clear boundaries. Lacking the drama, intensity, and enmeshment (over-involvement) of Stage 1 relationships, Stage 2 couples also may have less romance and intimacy. These couples tend to base their relationship on friendship and work on negotiation skills so that each member's needs are met. The desire for independence and control is present in Stage 2 relationships.

This level of relationship is critical in developing necessary skills for healthy relating. It is when people learn skills for communication, compromise, saying no, discussing issues, fighting in a fair way, working out disagreements, holding boundaries, and handling disappointments. This is when people learn how to give and take, and how to tolerate upsets while still being okay. These relationships are the most calm and stable, with low drama, low fighting, and low romantic excitement. This level is great for learning how to retain respect for oneself and others and how to not lose oneself in the relationship while still being able to give and relate.

As in the previous stage, the focus at this level of relationship is still on the self, and these relationships might be compared to a good partnership.

Can you describe or think of an example of a Stage 2 relationship? Can you think of an example on a TV show/media or something you have observed in your life?

_____

What do you think is the biggest challenge in these relationships?

_____

How do Stage 2 couples manage issues such as the desire to be right?

_____

Stage 3: Interdependence

Comparable to an "adult" stage of relationship development, Stage 3 relationships are both dependent and independent—they are interdependent. This means that each individual is grounded as an individual and also "loses" personal identity as he or she is part of a unit. Similar to being on a sports team, each member of the couple considers the good of the team (i.e., the household or relationship) before making decisions for one's own needs. These relationships are characterized by good communication between members, and the idea of mutual compromise and sacrifice—each giving a little and getting a little for the good of the relationship and of each other. Individuals are secure in themselves, so they are willing to put the relationship before the individual. At the same time, the relationship considers the needs of the individuals and therefore cares for the needs of everyone on the "team." Sometimes there are disagreements and upsets and this is part of negotiation and communication.

This stage in relationships is distinguished by mutual trust, caring, and respect, as well as intimacy and communication. These relationships are supportive and loving. They provide a solid foundation for raising children and pets, and handling other demands such as aging parents or taking on charity work. While the couple works well as a team, each member understands that not every need can be met by the other person, or by the relationship. The key is a combination of independence and closeness that is dynamic and interdependent.

Can you describe or think of an example of a Stage 3 relationship? Are there any good role models on TV/media or that you have observed in your life?

_____

What do you think is the biggest challenge in these relationships?

_____

How do Stage 3 couples manage issues such as the desire to be right?

_____

SOAP BUBBLES OF PERCEIVED REALITY

Imagine you are floating in a soap bubble, projecting your own perception of reality on the inside of the bubble and seeing the world through this lens. Others are also floating in their own bubbles, responding to their pasts and projecting their perceptions of reality on their own bubbles. As you can imagine, certain bubbles will automatically find each other and like a magnet will be drawn together. For example, dominant people will find submissive people, givers will find takers, and perfectionists will find criticizers! People have an uncanny way of attracting others to recreate their holograms.

If you want to attract different people in your life, then change what is being projected inside your own bubble!

STERNBERG'S TRIANGLES OF ROMANTIC LOVE

Psychologist Robert Sternberg (2004) theorizes that a relationship has three components: passion, intimacy, and commitment. Relationships that have a balance of all three components have a solid "consummate" love relationship.

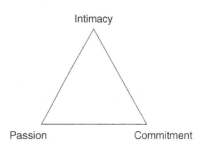

Some relationships have only one of these components or a combination of being strong in one or two areas and weak in another. "Intimacy only" is characterized by closeness, connectedness, and a sense of a good or best friend. "Commitment only" typically is a relationship by arrangement or agreement for benefits other than intimacy or passion (e.g., to unite two families, or share a common goal). "Infatuation," or "passion only," is physical passion, sexual attraction, and romance but no commitment or friendship. What do you think a Stage 1 relationship would look like on this triangle? How about Stages 2 and 3?

Sternberg's triangles can help you understand the quality of your relationship. Have you ever experienced one or two components without the other? Have you experienced a relationship that is strong in all three qualities?

Relationship Check-Up

If you speak up or disagree with your partner, and he or she gets angry because you disagree, what does that tell you about the relationship? What if you are afraid to upset your partner, so you agree to do things that you don't really want to do? What does that tell you about the relationship? To check in with yourself about your current relationship or consider those in the past, ask yourself the following true or false questions:

1. It was/is okay to need or want something from my partner and ask for it.
2. I can stand up for my own beliefs and disagree with my partner and still be accepted.
3. I can express my thoughts and feelings without worrying about it.
4. I may want to please my partner, but I don't have to please my partner all the time.

5. I can say "no" to my partner and my partner can say "no" to me without much upset.

6. I feel that my partner respects me and I respect my partner.

7. My partner and I compromise and make sure everyone's needs are met.

8. I can ask my partner for things without feeling bad, guilty, or worried.

9. I can give to my partner without feeling resentful, and my partner gives to me.

10. I am not afraid to be alone without any partner.

What do you think about your answers?

_____

What stage of relationship are you in now or have you been in previously?

_____

If you wanted to, what would you need to move to the next level?

_____

Exercise: Giving and Taking

Imbalanced relationships often consist of people who give too much and people who take too much. Are you a chronic giver or a chronic receiver? Consider these questions:

1. Do you give out of obligation or guilt?

2. Do you give with the expectation that other should or will reciprocate?

3. Do you give—or not—out of fear, anger, or jealousy?

4. Do you withhold giving because you expect others not to give to you?

It can be hard to know how much giving is enough, so it is worth giving these questions some thought in your relationships. It is important to take care of yourself—your needs, your dreams, your desires—so that you may give to other people. Balanced giving means considering both your own needs _and_ the needs of others.

Building Trusting Relationships

After sexual trauma, building trust in relationships can be especially difficult. By definition, you were violated, and your trust was betrayed by another person. This is a significant experience and naturally something that you would want to avoid in the future. Therefore, withdrawing from relationships or becoming isolated are common responses after sexual trauma. However, avoiding relationships does not heal the broken trust—it just prolongs the feeling that "it's not safe to trust."

The best way to heal is to realize that there are good people in the world, you do have good instincts, and you can build trust again. Start slowly—give a little and see how someone responds, then you can decide if this is someone you want to trust a little more. Trust builds with experiences and strengthens with time. You give a little, the other person gives a little . . . is there a general balance between giving and taking, trusting and sharing? What pattern develops over time? Is it balanced or lopsided? As you add new experiences, it is like placing a brick on your foundation. If you have a solid foundation, one little crack or upset (misunderstanding) will not break the whole foundation. The more you build positive experiences the stronger the bond.

Sometimes after trauma people develop rigid beliefs around trust. One crack—one disappointment, disagreement, slight, or perceived betrayal—and that is it! Relationship over! Cut and run . . . ! However, just because someone disappoints you does not mean they are completely untrustworthy or no longer your friend. Although it is true that there are some people you should never trust, most people are somewhere along a continuum, requiring time and experience to build trust. It is unrealistic to think you will only befriend people who will never upset you. People change plans, get busy, forget to return a call . . . so what does that mean? Is their heart in the right place but they are really busy, or does it mean that they disrespect you and are therefore unworthy? Do these things happen infrequently or chronically? What is okay and tolerable, and what is absolutely unacceptable? This requires personal soul-searching for you to determine if your boundary lines are too tight or too loose. Do you push people away, are you defensive, and do you keep a wall around your heart? Or do you allow anyone to come in, trample upon your heart, and take advantage of you?

Another thing to consider: Are you pushing someone away because of them, or is it because you are afraid of your own feelings? For example, what if you do let someone in? What if you do allow yourself to love again? What if the other person wants to have sex? If these questions make you panic and want to avoid the relationship, then what image is being generated in your mind? Are you being hurt, disrespected, or abused or feeling out of control, trapped, or afraid? Is it possible to change these negative images? What if you imagine having a *great* friendship or relationship? What would it be like if you were happy, and enjoyed intimacy and sex? What happens when you imagine a positive outcome?

Nobody knows for sure how people will behave. It helps to build trust over time and listen to your instincts. It also helps to have a balanced life— varied activities and social outlets—so that you are not completely dependent on one person or on one relationship.

Be careful! The wall of protection over time can turn into a wall of imprisonment. One previous participant said, "I still want my wall of protection, but now I have a door and a couple of windows."

LET'S TALK ABOUT SEX

When discussing healthy relationships, an important topic to address is sexual activity. Is there sex after sexual trauma? Some would say, "Of course," but many people would emphatically say, "No way!" However, this does not have to be the case. Although it is true that many survivors of sexual trauma have experienced difficulties with sex, it is also possible to heal in this area. The most common symptoms reported after sexual trauma are an intense fear of sex, decreased arousal and desire, decreased frequency of intimate contact (or none at all), decreased satisfaction and pleasure, and avoidance of sexual contact. Some women report that sex can be painful, some men may experience erectile dysfunction, and both men and women may not be able to have orgasms. These are reasonable and typical reactions. In fact, it is unrealistic and puts an unfair burden on you to think you shouldn't have any sexual issues, and that it is somehow your obligation to perform or please others regardless of how you feel. This would certainly increase anxiety around sex and be counterproductive to healing. As we've been discussing "rewiring" the brain, so too can sex be "rewired" from something painful, out of your control, and hateful to something gentle, pleasurable, and loving. Sexual healing is learning how to feel safe, comfortable, and relaxed with your own body as well as with someone else to the extent that the focus moves away from "performing or achieving" and toward loving and sharing intimacy. This is a gentle process and should be done at your own pace and comfort level, using good communication with your partner.

For Those Not in a Relationship or Planning on Ever Being in One

It may appear that a conversation about sex does not apply to you because you are perfectly comfortable not being in a romantic relationship and have no plans to change that. This is not uncommon and completely understandable. Saying no to intimate relationships is a place of safety, comfort, and control. It protects you from becoming involved in a Stage 1 relationship that will probably end poorly. It also protects you from getting hurt, disappointed, and betrayed. For some, sexual trauma caused physical damage and the thought of sex is painful or "impossible." However, maybe one day you may meet someone that you really like. Reading this discussion about sex can open the possibility that maybe, sometime in the future, you may want to have a relationship again. Hopefully, this discussion will demystify the fears associated with sex. *Note:* There are no rights or wrongs, judgments, or shoulds or shouldn'ts about being single or in a couple. The goal is to give you freedom of choice.

Ground Rules and Agreements

Sex begins before any physical contact ever occurs. It is something that two people agree upon in the context of their relationship. Similar to the levels of relationships previously discussed, as you become more comfortable, secure, and trusting of yourself you will attract relationships that match your level of development and readiness for intimacy. Sexuality is a developmental process that can unfold to the level of the quality of the relationship. What kind of sexual experiences would you expect at Stage 1, 2, and 3 relationships?

Sex at Stage 1_____

Sex at Stage 2_____

Sex at Stage 3_____

Wendy Maltz (2012) has developed a model to help couples establish safety in the bedroom. The "CERTS" model stands for *consent* (partners both consent to sexual activity and either can stop it at any time), *equality* (both are equal participants with neither dominating or intimidating), *respect* (both participants respect each other and feel respected by each other), *trust* (both partners trust each other on a physical and emotional level, and respond to concerns with sensitivity), and *safety* (both participants feel safe and secure in the setting and from any consequences such as unwanted pregnancy, infections, or injury). She believes this sets a necessary foundation, context, and agreement for participating in any sexual activity at any level. It also sets a foundation for healing sexual issues after trauma.

Common Symptoms in the Bedroom

Because the trauma occurred in a sexual context, anything related to sex could be a trigger or reminder of the trauma. Even if you are not consciously thinking about the trauma, it is not uncommon to suddenly feel intensely afraid; have tense muscles or pain; cry; not want to be touched at all; feel trapped; have difficulty breathing; feel ashamed, embarrassed, or confused; and not be aroused or feel any pleasure. You may find that you are enjoying intimacy and all of a sudden need to stop. There may be certain touches, positions, sounds, or smells that may trigger anxiety, anger, or the desire to scream, run, or hide. This could be caused by a body memory, a moment of dissociation (feeling detached from your body or the experience), an intrusive thought or worry, or simply feeling uncomfortable. Have any of these experiences ever happened to you? If so, you are not alone. Even if you have a loving partner, it is possible that all of a sudden you may feel that part of you is re-experiencing the past. This is not your fault and it is not your partner's fault—but rather part of the wiring or associations that have been made between trauma and sex.

How to Handle Triggers and Anxiety Related to Sexual Activity

If and when triggers happen, it is important to frame them as fleeting experiences (although uncomfortable) and they will pass. *Cleansing breaths* are helpful and anything else that brings you comfort such as hugging a pillow, hugging or being hugged by a partner (if that feels good), smelling something pleasant, or taking a walk. Remind yourself that you are in the here and now, safe, and okay. You can use your COPE strategy until the feeling passes (remember: cleansing breath, observation, positive self-talk, and explanation).

If you do become triggered before, during, or after sexual activity, it may be an indicator that you need to slow down and work with your partner—communicate and discuss how you can help each other and support each other. You are not obligated to have sex or engage in any activity that you don't want to. If you are being triggered, then it would make sense to stop and refrain from sex for a while. This is not avoiding the issue, but rather it removes an active trigger while you work on other aspects of the relationship.

Emphasis on Intimacy Instead of Sex

To begin thinking about sexual healing, let's first consider what is typically regarded as sexual activity: "foreplay leading to intercourse, leading to orgasm, followed by some cuddling." However, in this book we will *redefine* sexual activity as an act of expressing intimacy with another person. If the experience is really about intimacy, then the pressure of "sex" is removed from the equation. Instead, intimacy begins with a good relationship, laughter, doing nice things for each other, holding hands, cuddling, eye-gazing, and just breathing together. Physical contact can be incorporated in safe, non-threatening ways such as foot, hand, and arm massages. Touch can be enjoyed with or without becoming sexual. In fact, some sex treatments, such as in the *sensate focus technique*, require a strict "no touch zone" for sensitive areas when first learning how to give and receive touch. In sensate focus, couples are *not* allowed to have sex (or touch sexual body parts) but instead go through a mutlistage process of learning how to touch, hug, and be with each other. It starts with hugging and touching fully clothed and then progresses, depending on the pace of the couple, to unclothed. The point is to shift the focus from the demands and anxiety of sex to enjoying being with the other person. Intimacy is meant to be fun, playful, romantic, relaxing, and special. Intimacy is about loving and being loved. In other words, with patience, communication, and going at your own comfortable pace, intimacy can be incorporated into your relationship, thereby increasing safety, trust, and ultimately arousal.

The couple should also discuss how they feel about initiating touch or intimacy. Some MST survivors are triggered if their partner initiates touch. They may feel taken off guard—leading to fearful instead of amorous feelings. There may also be certain types of touches or places that are particular triggers. This should also be discussed.

DISCLOSURE ABOUT PAST TRAUMAS

One issue participants bring up is if they should tell their partner about their sexual trauma, and if so, what should they say? This is an excellent question.

While only you can answer to whom, how much, and when you want to disclose your story, there are several things to consider around the issue of disclosure. First of all, your partner is not a trained therapist, may not know how to respond, and will likely have his or her own reactions and feelings about it. Second, it is important to be clear why you want to tell your partner—is it to improve your communication regarding sexual intimacy or is it a desire to have someone listen to you and help you process your feelings? Again, your partner is not a therapist. Be careful if you have certain expectations from your partner, as he or she may not give you the response you want. Do not assume your partner will know how to handle your disclosure. Some common responses that partners could have include feeling helpless, angry, anxious, uncomfortable, or confused; not knowing what to say or do; and maybe being afraid. He or she might say something blaming or hurtful because he or she doesn't know how to handle his or her feelings. He or she may want to get revenge on the perpetrator, or may minimize the trauma completely.

But this doesn't mean don't disclose—it just means think about what you say and how you say it. In fact, there could be consequences if you choose not to disclose. Maybe your partner takes it personally if you don't want to have sex. Maybe your partner worries that he or she is not attractive, is not loved, or that you are having an affair. Without an explanation, people start to worry and create their own explanations. Have you ever had an experience like this? Not disclosing can cause broken relationships and a host of misunderstandings.

So, there is not an easy answer—and avoidance certainly does not solve this issue. If you choose to disclose, be aware of what you want to achieve by disclosing. In addition, you don't have to share all the details to get your main point across. In fact, many partners would rather not know specific details. If you guide your partner and say, "I'm telling you this because this is what I need from you," and let him or her know how to help you, what to do or not to do, while being considerate of your partner's feelings, then disclosure can be a tender and intimate exchange.

Considerations for Disclosure

1. *Quality of the relationship.* Is this your first date or have you known this person for a while and have established a friendship? Do you trust this person? Have you "tested the waters" by disclosing less threatening or less sensitive things? How has your partner handled other sensitive things that you have shared about yourself? Has your partner disclosed personal information to you?

2. *Readiness to engage in sexual activity.* Are you ready to take the relationship to the next level sexually? Are you feeling pressure to have sex before you are ready (too soon)? Do you think if you have sex it will make you feel loved? Have you had positive intimacy experiences, including foreplay? Do you feel there is consent, equality, respect, trust, and safety in the relationship?

3. *Time and place.* Disclosure of past sexual trauma is not something to discuss during sex or sexual intimacy. Rather, it's best to disclose when you are fully dressed in a safe, nonthreatening situation so you can talk about it safely, without distractions or interruptions, and with privacy. Is your partner tired, distracted, or watching a ball game, or is he or she ready to hear you and completely focused on the conversation? Are you in a safe environment?

4. *Know your desired outcome before disclosing.* Why are you telling someone about what happened to you? What do you hope to gain/ achieve from the conversation? You can even let your partner know why you want to share and what you are hoping for. Also, read the signs during the conversation. If it is not going well, you can stop and take a break.

5. *Don't disclose more than you feel comfortable.* You can, but you don't have to disclose what happened. Regardless of whether you do or do not disclose, you still can discuss what you want or don't want in the bedroom and you still are not obligated to do anything that you don't want to do. You can say you are not comfortable with something without an explanation.

6. *Be prepared to help your partner.* When you disclose, be prepared to help your partner process his or her feelings about it, to answer questions, and offer guidance and reassurance. It may seem counterintuitive because the trauma happened to you, but now it is something that affects both of you. You've already processed and thought about it (probably for several years), but this is brand new for your partner and he or she may need some help.

7. *Consider couples therapy.* Therapy can help couples through challenging parts of their relationship. A therapist can help you navigate through communication blocks and can help couples establish a safe, trusting, loving, and sexual relationship.

Tips for a Positive, Loving Sexual Experience

- Work on a good friendship—share, laugh, trust, and enjoy each other.
- Work on communication—discussing, respecting, and upholding boundaries; negotiation; handling disagreements; and considering your needs as well as your partner's.
- Talk openly about sex—what is okay, what is not, and what each of you needs/wants.
- Make sure there is consent, equality, respect, trust, and safety (CERTS) in the relationship and in the bedroom.
- Be patient with yourself, your partner, and the process.

- If you let your partner know that you experienced sexual trauma and sex is a trigger for you, discuss what makes you comfortable and how your partner can help you. What is arousing and what is anxiety-provoking?
- Discuss expectations around sex. What agreements will make you feel comfortable? Discuss concerns around obligations, expectations, need to achieve orgasm, or any other "requirements" for sexual activity.
- Increase your focus on intimacy—sharing, touching, caring, and loving.

Finally, it is important to separate your experiences of unwanted sexual trauma from new experiences of mutually consensual sex. Sharing sex with a partner is a very different experience and hopefully one that is loving and positive. It is normal to want to have sex and it is also normal to want it in a way that makes you feel safe and comfortable. If you need to stop or decline sexual activity, this is something that should be discussed and understood by both partners—understanding that it is not something you are doing to be mean, manipulative, or withholding; nor is it something a partner should use against you to try to make you feel guilty (e.g., accusing you of depriving, neglecting, or being hurtful). Your sex life is not just about you or just about your partner; it is about both of you. When you address this issue together and work on intimacy and safety, then both of you will reap the benefits of a loving relationship.

Writing exercise: **Take a few moments to think about "an ideal relationship." How would you like to treat each other? Not only in positive ways, but also how you would like to negotiate and handle disagreements, conflicts, chores, and communication. Describe how you would like intimacy in the relationship. Think of the three stages of relationships and other information in this chapter. Write your description here.**

_____

_____

_____

_____

_____

_____

_____

THOUGHTS ABOUT LOVE

What if everyone is born valuable and loveable? In other words, consider this: You are fundamentally a worthy, beautiful human being. In fact, we really can't even fathom how incredible it is to be a human being. Our potential is immeasurable. It is acknowledged that we do make choices, and some are more positive than others. People make mistakes and poor choices. Those are behaviors. Behaviors come and go, even consequences can change, but your essence, regardless of your behaviors, is constant. When we discuss your worth or value, that transcends your behaviors. When you forgive yourself of all past behaviors, you can wipe your slate clean and start again. Remembering "your essence" or "that which is you" is the key to this process. You are still you, the person before the trauma, before feeling abused, and before withdrawing or running from your feelings. Nothing can touch your inner essence of life—the light of life, if you will, that is inside of you. When you can let go of anger, hurt, and resentment; forgive yourself for mistakes; and love yourself through shame, guilt, and grief, you can clear the way for the glowing light to shine again. It is already in you, it has always been you, and is always with you. Maybe you have forgotten your glowing light within, maybe it wasn't safe to glow when you were a child, or in the military. Maybe you disconnected from the awareness of your inner self because you were in an environment that did not love or nurture you.

The fact is, we are prewired at a deep level to respond to love. The attachment research demonstrates the innate desire and response of humans (and primates) to respond to emotional connection or what we may define as love. If you didn't experience warm, loving, supportive relationships in your family, in the military, or in your adult relationships, it makes sense to want to protect yourself, and in doing so, try to cover up or deny that part of you that ultimately craves these loving relationships. This is how people come to believe that love is some elusive experience outside of them. This is how people come to believe negative falsehoods about themselves.

Imagine, if you will, how you might feel if a fundamental part of you was love. If this were the case, then love is not something outside of you, something to find, something to hold onto, or something that can be lost; it is not in someone else or only found in the excitement of romance. What if . . . love is always inside of you? When you connect with others you share love because it already exists in you—just like it exists in them. Sharing love reminds you that it is there! It is impossible to lose it because it is part of who you are. Imagine how powerful, safe, and comforting that would feel. . . . How would it influence the choices you make and the behaviors that you do? How would it change how you perceive others? If others are negative, then you can see how disconnected they are from themselves. How would that change how you respond?

CHAPTER 10 SUMMARY POINTS

- There are three levels of relationships from a developmental model: Stage 1 is Dependent, Stage 2 is Independent, and Stage 3 is Interdependent.

- Good relationships are a balance of giving and taking. Balance is an active process that requires attention and adjustments.

- Trust builds with positive experiences over time.

- Healthy sex means taking the pressure off of sexual performance and instead focusing on improving intimacy.

- Should you disclose to a new partner about your past trauma? The choice is yours, but there are several things to consider such as the quality of your relationship, what you hope to gain from the disclosure, and being prepared to support your partner with his or her reactions, questions, and concerns.

- Sex is enhanced by good communication, mutual respect, patience, removing pressures or obligations, and focusing on intimacy, sharing, and loving each other.

- You are already prewired to respond to love! When you connect with this part of yourself, you will feel the benefits of feeling content, relaxed, peaceful, and happy. Imagine focusing on a warm, glowing light coming from your heart. Imagine it and see how you feel!

Effective Communication

11

with Jane Hammerslough

> You can't not communicate. Everything you say and do or don't say and don't do sends a message to others.
>
> —*John Woods*

- *Opening exercises: Interactive communication exercises*
  (Day 1 and Day 2: Vocal warm-up exercises)
- *Closing exercises: Staying grounded and energy cleansing*
  (Day 1: Staying grounded, Day 2: Energy cleansing)

At the core of a healthy relationship is good communication. In this chapter we will explore various aspects of communication followed by specific skills to improve communication.

Communication is the process of sharing and exchanging information. It involves a "transmitter" who gives information, and a "receiver" who receives the information. In a conversation, two people take turns being the transmitter and receiver. In this chapter we will define good communication as "effective," meaning that the message that is being transmitted is received in the way that it is intended. Like in a game of catch, when one person throws a ball and the other catches it without any trouble, we would say that the exchange of the ball was complete. Similarly, when someone "throws" a communication and the intended person receives it accurately, then we would say it was effective communication.

But this requires several elements. First of all, the throw needs to be a good throw. This means good aim (e.g., directing the communication to the right person), good strength, not being too hard or too soft (e.g., appropriate emotional power), and good intention (being responsible for the message being delivered). The hope is that a good throw will be matched with a good

Adapted from Katz and Hammerslough (2012).

catch. If the communication is not caught, then it doesn't matter how great the throw is! Ideally, the communication is received in the way it was intended—producing the desired results. So by definition, the effective delivery of a message needs to be met with effective listening and understanding. In summary, effective communication includes good throws and good catches.

Effective communication is communication
that is received in the way it is intended.

SENDING AND RECEIVING MESSAGES

Read each example and then enact the toss between two people in the group to demonstrate the example. If you don't have a ball, improvise and toss something that is light and easy to catch.

Example 1: Person A has a ball and tosses it to Person B. Person A has every intention of getting it to Person B, and Person B has every intention of receiving it. However, sometimes even with good intentions, the ball is dropped.

Example 2: Person A throws the ball without any attention to Person B. The ball is tossed far away from Person B. Person B may try very hard, but may still be unable to catch the ball.

Example 3: Person A carefully tosses the ball to Person B. However, Person B is distracted and makes no effort to catch the ball. The ball is dropped.

These examples illustrate that in order to complete a catch it takes both a good toss and a good catch, and sometimes a little luck! Communication requires the cooperation between a sender and receiver to make it work. Effective communication is a message that is sent and received without the ball dropping.

The second part of our definition is that effective communication is not only received, but it is done so in the way that it is intended. This is not always obvious because people can either send mixed messages or people can receive a message and interpret it in a different way than it was intended! In addition, when emotions are running high, people are likely to react quickly without really thinking about what the other person is *intending* to say. With all these factors, no wonder it is so easy to have miscommunications.

THE MANY FACETS OF COMMUNICATION

One reason that confusion may occur in communication is that it is composed of many different elements. There are four key facets of communication: words, tone, emphasis, and body language.

Words

The words you choose are important, because they provide shades of meaning. Many different words may mean basically the same thing, but when used in the same sentences, may communicate subtle differences. For example, consider the different shades of meaning in this sentence when you substitute the words "odor," "smell," "scent," and "fragrance" for "X" in this sentence: "Her X was extraordinary." How do each of these sentences say the same thing? How do they communicate extremely different messages? It depends on your interpretation, of course—and how the words are heard. There are some words, however, that may strike a chord no matter who is talking. These include "always" and "never." How does it feel when someone says, "You always..." or "You never..."? Effective communication means considering the impact of words before you make statements that are extreme and/or untrue.

Tone

You can whisper or shout, or anything in between, and what you say will have a different impact. In the same way, every tone—from questioning to emphatic, from timid to confident—conveys something different. Becoming conscious of your tone, both in volume and inflection, can help you learn to communicate in the way in which you want to be understood. Tone can convey a wide range of meanings using the exact same words! A tone can sound disapproving, surprised, pleased, or express any other emotion.

Emphasis

The way you emphasize words in a sentence can change its meaning in dramatic ways. Like tone, it relies on volume and inflection to change meaning, but with emphasis it is all about context in a sentence.

Body Language

Body language is the catchall term for nonverbal communication created through your face and body, such as posture, facial expression, and positioning of your arms and hands. Body language may tell someone that you are interested, alert, and willing to hear new things, or that you are uninterested, bored, or defensive. It may be consistent with what you say you feel or convey something quite the opposite! The way you use your body in conversation may communicate some things that you do not intend to communicate. Cultivating awareness of your body language is an important part of becoming a more effective communicator. Once you know what you might be projecting nonverbally, you can better control the message you send to others, and increase the likelihood of being understood in the way you want to be heard.

The goal of working on your body language is to accurately present what you wish to present. The common issue, however, is that we say one thing—and our bodies may say something else. For example, how many times have you ever heard someone say, "I'm fine," but her arms crossed in front of her chest, chin jutting out, and clenched fists say something totally different?

USING WORDS, TONE, EMPHASIS, AND BODY LANGUAGE

The following is a group exercise. Everyone stands in a circle. Following the instructions for each round, everyone in the group takes a turn going around in a circle.

Round 1

For this exercise, everyone says the same word, "Oh," but by varying the tone see how many different ways this one word can sound, each one conveying a slightly different meaning.

Round 2

Everyone says the phrase: "Did you take the garbage out?" but emphasizes a different word in the phrase. Explore how emphasis changes the meaning of the same set of words.

Round 3

Discover the power of body language by using the body to express emotions without any words or sounds. In this exercise everyone uses their body to make a "statue" (i.e., strike a posture and then freeze). Do this several times to express the following: anger, forgiveness, shame, disapproval, and being at peace. See if the group can generate a few more emotions they might want to try. Notice all the ways these emotions are expressed using gestures, stance, facial expressions, and other body postures.

Round 4

In this final round, participants can use tone, emphasis, and body language to express a variety of things using the following phrase: "But I said I was fine!" Notice how confusing it is to interpret what people are really expressing when their words say "fine," but their tone, emphasis, and body language say otherwise.

Imagine trying to communicate when people are sending two or more messages (i.e., mixed messages)! It's like throwing two balls at the same time in opposite directions and saying, "Catch!" And then being disappointed, angry, or frustrated when the receiver doesn't catch the ball . . . or worse, catches one ball but not the one the tosser secretly was hoping he or she would catch! Sometimes when people send mixed messages they hope the person will figure out what they really want to express. This is gambling with low odds and more often than not will lead to arguments, hurt feelings, misinterpretation, and certainly confusion.

It's difficult enough trying to communicate, but your odds will increase substantially when you become aware of your feelings and check yourself to see if you are sending a clear message. If the communication is not received in the way you intended, then either your message was not clear, or the person was not ready or able to receive it. Remember it takes two to get a message across.

Did You Know . . .

Facial expressions, gestures, posture, eye contact, touch, and the personal space that exists between two people are all forms of nonverbal communication that may speak volumes. Not only are there different expectations and meanings from culture to culture or between geographical locations, but there are also differences between men and women, and contextual factors (e.g., being familiar or formal). Being able to send and receive nonverbal cues accurately is an important skill.

RIGHTS AND RESPONSIBILITIES

Effective communication begins with two key concepts: rights and responsibilities. Each of us has the right to express ourselves. At various times you may have felt "silenced," misunderstood, or simply unable to communicate for one reason or another. You may have said "yes" when you meant "no," and "no" when you wanted to say "yes." While it is common to have experienced these feelings or situations at one time or another, everyone has the right to free expression.

At the same time, everyone also must take responsibility for what is said and how it was said. To do this, it is important to cultivate consciousness of your own communication. That means to be aware of what you feel, aware of others, and aware of the situation. It means being authentic and true to yourself and honest with others, while also being responsible for the impact of your words on others. Just because you think or feel something does not mean you should say it without regard for other people's feelings. At the same time, you are not obligated to please everyone either. It is a balance between expressing yourself honestly and being respectful of others, while not (over)assuming responsibility for other people's feelings (e.g., feeling obligated or guilty).

Where are you in terms of this balance? How often do you do each of the following? Put an X under the term that describes your behavior.

	Frequently	Sometimes	Infrequently
Express myself honestly	_____	_____	_____
Consider others' feelings	_____	_____	_____
Assume responsibility for others	_____	_____	_____

Being responsible can also mean becoming aware of mixed messages and whether you are sending them unintentionally. It can also mean considering the ways we sometimes hear what we want to hear—and not what another person intends to communicate. It also means thinking about nonverbal communication or "body language" used to convey something—sometimes hoping people will just "know" how you feel.

Being an effective communicator means being able to accurately read a situation and those involved, and draw upon inner resources to be able to communicate in the most effective way. An effective communicator is wise and considers one's own feelings, other people's feelings, and the potential consequences of the communication. In other words, before speaking, it is an effective communicator who considers if it is the best time and place to do so, while balancing the need to stay true to oneself and respect others.

As one participant said:

Say what you mean, mean what you say, and don't say it meanly!

Did You Know . . .

Body language and tone may give an indication of certain communication styles.

Passive communicators may slump, have poor eye contact, and speak softly.

Aggressive communicators thrust out their chests in an overbearing way, have very direct eye contact, and speak loudly.

Assertive communicators generally make good eye contact, have good posture, and speak in a normal and calm vocal tone.

A WORD ON LISTENING

Business leader Stephen R. Covey (1989) identified an important aspect of communication when writing about the seven habits of highly effective people: "Seek first to understand, then to be understood." Though sometimes overlooked in discussions of making ourselves heard in the best way possible, active and empathic listening is one of the most important skills in effective communication. Think of how it feels to have a conversation with a person who doesn't listen—or listens poorly. We have all been there at one time or another! Poor listeners come in many varieties, from the people who interrupt (or never stop talking themselves long enough for you to say anything) to those who ask questions but pay no attention to your responses, to those who are just plain distracted during conversations. These conversations are frustrating, at best. Poor listening skills may or may not be the result of someone not being interested in what we have to say—but it can sure seem that way!

On the other hand, actively listening to another person helps you gather information that you might overlook when you don't pay close attention. It conveys both a sense of self-respect—you take conversations seriously enough to fully engage in them—and, equally important, it communicates a sense of respect for another person. Listening—and showing that you are interested in their message—can help validate another person's feelings, which can help them become less defensive and more open to what you have to say. Actively listening and trying to understand can radically change the tone of an entire conversation in a more positive direction.

One way to actively listen is to "check in" to make sure that you are understanding what the other person is saying—*before* you respond. Repeating what a person says back to him or her so that you are clear on your message is a good way to communicate that you understand. It also provides the person with an opportunity to correct him- or herself, and clarify what he or she means to communicate.

To say that a person feels listened to means a lot more than just their ideas get heard. It's a sign of respect. It makes people feel valued.
—*Deborah Tannen*

3-Minute Listening Exercise

Everyone finds a partner and sits facing across from each other. One person is A and the other is B. A spends the next 3 minutes talking about whatever he or she wants. B listens. B cannot respond verbally but can nod or communicate nonverbally. At the end of 3 minutes B summarizes what A said. If A wants to clarify something, then A can. B confirms that the communication was heard by summarizing it again. Then A and B repeat the exercise, but switching roles. Afterwards the group discusses their experience.

EXERCISES IN EFFECTIVE COMMUNICATION

How do you handle challenging interpersonal situations? In the next sections, several exercises will be presented to practice effective communication. These exercises will help you explore how and why you may respond the way you do—and what that might communicate (or not communicate) to another person. They will also help you learn, practice, and develop communication skills. These exercises are highly interactive and experiential in nature, with the intention of being fun!

For some of these, a "therapeutic theater" is created. There is a stage and an audience. Each participant will take a turn on stage, and when not on stage can participate as an active audience member. In most of the exercises there will be two people on stage. One of them will be an antagonist (the "villain," or someone playing a difficult character) and the other person is the protagonist (the "hero," or the one attempting to work out a positive solution).

In these exercises, the person playing the protagonist is being herself. However, the person playing the antagonist is playing a *role* and is not really that person.

For safety reasons, there are a few rules that everyone should agree to before setting up a therapeutic stage. First of all, there is no yelling, swearing, or pushing. In other words, everyone has to agree to treat each other with respect and remember that this is *only a role-play*! Second, there is no magic. The protagonist can't wave a magic wand and make things different. Third, the facilitator is the director and can give commands such as "freeze" or "cut" to interrupt or end a scene.

Scenario 1: Returning an Item to a Store

In this scene, the protagonist is returning an item to a store. She has a complaint about the product and goes to the customer service department, but encounters a difficult, uncooperative employee. How can the protagonist walk away satisfied with the outcome of the interaction? Using the skills of assertive communication can help.

Assertive communication qualities and skills include:

- Speaking calmly and clearly
- Stating needs and wants clearly and in a respectful manner
- Not interrupting others
- Feeling a sense of control and exhibiting self-control
- Standing up for oneself; not letting others intimidate or manipulate
- Taking responsibility for oneself
- Maintaining composure in stressful situations
- Exhibiting confidence in one's own opinions and abilities but being open to other ideas

With these qualities in mind, practice this role play. Vary the scenario: For example, the protagonist does not have a receipt, the item is broken, or the item has been used or half eaten. In one scene, the antagonist is rude and defensive, and in another is disengaged and distracted. How does the protagonist handle the situation? The facilitator ends the scenes and invites comments from the spectators. What skills seemed to work well? What didn't work very well?

When the scene is complete, the protagonist invites someone from the audience to play the antagonist role and the former antagonist becomes the protagonist in the next scene. Continue until everyone has a chance to participate in both roles.

Rotation:

1. Antagonist and protagonist role play scene.

2. Protagonist picks someone in the audience to come up and be the new antagonist.

3. Previous antagonist is the new protagonist.

I think the one lesson I have learned is that there is no substitute for paying attention.
—Diane Sawyer

SPEAKING YOUR TRUTH

In this section, we will explore various common challenges in communication, such as how to handle a situation when you feel cornered or pressured to make a quick decision or what to do when someone says something rude or disrespectful to you. These are situations when an automatic response may lead to a communication that you later regret, such as agreeing to do something you really don't want to do or saying something that leads to escalating an argument. Effective communicators keep their cool and think before responding. This section will present a variety of techniques for handling requests and de-escalateing potential arguments.

Part 1: Handling Requests

In this next section, we will be exploring how to handle requests. Sometimes people feel obligated or pressured to answer on the spot or to say yes to things they really don't want to do. And sometimes that pressured answer results in people feeling angry or resentful. How do you make the decision that is right for you, regardless of the situation? Several techniques will be presented.

Skill 1: "Let Me Think About It"

When you clearly want to do something or don't want to do something, then it is easy to respond (e.g., yes or no). However, what if you are not sure or are having mixed feelings and thoughts about it? It can be both difficult and frustrating to feel you should say yes when you want to say no—this is where the five "magic" words *"Let me think about it"* can be so useful. "Let me think about it" can help you handle any request and respond the way *you* want to handle it. "Let me think about it" gives you time to tune in and see how you really feel. It enables you to weigh your options and remove the "now or never" pressure of responding. You can consider both your needs as well as the other person's. Chances are that you will find the right answer for how you really feel—and discover what you really want to do.

Another phrase that can help you when you are clear that you want to end further discussion or demands is *"It's just not possible."* This sentence presents a firm and complete stance that is not open to further discussion, but it is not insulting or alienating to others.

Tips to remember:

1. Remember that you are not responsible for fixing or solving someone else's emergency. The situation probably did not suddenly occur, but rather there was a long build-up before it became a crisis.

2. Just because someone asks you for a favor does not mean you have to grant it. He or she can always ask someone else.

3. If you say "no" it does not mean you are obligated to problem solve and find another solution. You can simply say "no."

4. Helping someone is distinct from enabling them to continue irresponsible behavior.

5. On the other hand, if you can help and you have considered your needs (e.g., time and resources) and considered the other person's needs, you may want to help.

6. People who are manipulative will sometimes bring in others (either in person or in spirit) to make requests or demands on their behalf—"John would really like it if you would give me some money," for example, or "I would do this for you. . . ." These phrases can put you on the defensive and make you feel guilty. But remember you are only responsible for you and they are responsible for getting themselves into a pickle. You friendship does not require that you stop whatever you are doing, "lend" your money away, or engage in unpleasant favors. Others are free to ask things, but it is ultimately ALWAYS your decision.

The Power of "No"

Many of us have a hard time saying no to requests from others. This is because we sometimes confuse saying no with a fear of people not liking us. This could have been learned from an early age—that we should be agreeable, helpful, and pleasing, regardless of our true feelings. The heart of effective communication is authenticity—being true to ourselves. "No" is just a word that sets a clear boundary that can help get our own needs met. It's okay to say no! Saying "no" from a position of positivity and strength can help enhance self-esteem and decrease resentment.

Skill 2: Broken Record

Do you remember vinyl records? Most people don't have records or record players (turn-tables) anymore . . . and some people have never even seen one! But records were very popular for several decades. Music was imprinted on the vinyl in thin grooves that encircled the disk. The way it worked was as the record spun around on a turntable, a tiny needle vibrated between the grooves. The sound was then amplified and sent through speakers. Records were big and rather delicate. If it got scratched, the needle would be stuck in the same groove. That section of music would play over and over again.

The *broken record* technique (which maybe should be renamed the scratched CD technique!) is similar to the sound of a broken or scratched record. When someone makes a request and the recipient is clear on the answer, he or she simply repeats the answer over and over again. This is an excellent technique when someone is being pushy or relentless. Some people think if they keep asking it will "wear down" the individual and eventually he or she will give in. The broken record technique gives a clear and firm message . . . eventually the one asking gets the message and usually will stop.

Challenging Requests

People use a variety of tactics to get others to agree to their requests. They might use guilt, such as saying, "If you loved me you would do this for me," "I would do this for *you*, so you should do it for me," or "I thought you were a good friend, but maybe I was mistaken." These are untrue statements with a specific intent to force the other person to agree. The truth is, love has nothing to do with the request! These tactics are obvious, especially if the receiver feels guilt, pressure, or obligation. However, some tactics are more subtle, including the "foot-in-the-door" and "door-in-the-face" strategies.

Foot-in-the-Door

The *foot-in-the-door* technique was based on Fuller Brush salesmen who would go door-to-door to sell brooms and brushes. The salesmen would knock on the door and when the resident opened the door, he would slip his foot across the threshold so that if the resident tried to close the door, his foot would prevent it from closing! Although door-to-door salesmen are mostly a thing of the past, this technique is alive and well in advertising and marketing today. How often have we all bought something "extra" that we probably didn't need or want because it seemed like a good deal?

This has become a strategy based on the idea that if someone agrees to one thing, then they will most likely agree to something else. For example, if someone agrees to buy an item, then the sales person might say, "Well, for only $2.00 more, you can get this upgrade!" Foot-in-the-door is a strategy that can be tricky to navigate, because it often happens quickly, can be confusing, and before you know it, you have agreed to something that you had no intention of agreeing to. It happens in sales as well as in interactions with others. For example, let's say Donna asks Jerry if he would go shopping with her to help her carry her bags, noting that he could do some shopping as well. He agrees to go with her. Then she asks if he could drive. He has already agreed to one request (and is invested in the event), so he may be more likely to agree to the second request.

Door-in-the-Face

The *door-in-the-face* technique is another manipulative method of getting others to agree to a request. In this strategy, a big request is followed by a smaller one. For example, if someone asks if they can borrow $100 and you say no, they immediately follow the request with, "Okay, I understand, but can I borrow $10?" The larger request makes the second one seem more manageable—and therefore you are more likely to say yes.

This technique may work because we somehow feel obligated to do *something* for someone else. After saying no to a large request, we may actually experience a sense of relief at "getting off easy" by only having to lend the person $10. Another example: Matt asks you for a ride to the airport, which is about an hour away. You want to help Matt, but that's 2 hours of driving assuming there is no traffic. He sees you hesitating and says, "Well, there is a bus that goes to the airport, can you drive me to the bus stop, which is less than 10 minutes away?" The door-in-the-face is another technique that can be difficult to handle, because we may have conflicting feelings over saying no. We may actually want to help. Or we may just want the person—and their problem—to go away. No matter how you feel, it can be hard to handle door-in-the-face requests because they, too, occur quickly, and before you know it, you have agreed to something that you may not really want to do.

Scenario 2: Handling Requests

To practice your effective communication skills in handling requests, set up a scenario where one person asks another for a favor. In this exercise, the antagonist uses multiple techniques including manipulation, guilt, foot-in-the-door, and door-in-the-face to try to get something from the protagonist. It may be to borrow some money or to ask for another favor. The protagonist answers (as herself) and can say, "Yes," "No," "Let me think about it," and can use the broken record technique. Do several rounds so that everyone has an opportunity to participate.

Make the scene increasingly more outrageous. The antagonist can ask for a small favor or a ridiculous favor. For example: "Can I borrow $5 for lunch?" "Oh good, then can I also borrow $500 to pay my phone bill so my phone doesn't get turned off?" "Can you babysit my nephew tonight?" "Can you drive me to the airport?" "Can I borrow your car for the weekend?" "Can I stay on your couch so I can save some money to go on a cruise?" "Can I borrow your boyfriend to take me to my cousin's wedding—in Hawaii?" The protagonist can say *"Yes," "No,"* or *"Let me think about it."*

Afterward, ask the spectators what worked and what didn't. Did you notice if the protagonist started to feel obligated, guilty, or pressured to want to agree to the request? Was this at the expense of her well-being? Did you notice any behaviors or communications from the protagonist that would convey to the antagonist that with a little more effort she might get the protagonist to agree? In other words, notice if body language, words, tone, and emphasis are all conveying the same message or if the protagonist is giving mixed messages and not even aware of it!

Let various people take turns being the antagonist, protagonist, and spectators. Continue with the exercise and add the technique of broken record, such as repeating the phrase "It's just not possible" or "My answer is no, I don't lend money." Notice how it feels saying it, receiving it, and watching others use this technique.

As before, when the scene is complete, the protagonist invites someone from the audience to play the antagonist role and the former antagonist becomes the protagonist in the next scene. Continue until everyone has a chance to participate in both roles.

> Courage is what it takes to stand up and speak.
> Courage is also what it takes to sit down and listen.
> —*Winston Churchill*

"BAITING" AND ESCALATIONS

Often requests involve being "baited"—as if someone casts out a line with a big, fat, juicy worm to try to get the other person to bite. Baiting means setting someone up to feel or act a certain way. It is a form of manipulation. For example, someone might bait another person into a fight with an attack by "pushing their buttons" or saying something provocative or upsetting. If the person takes the bait, then he or she becomes "hooked." Once she is hooked on the line the other person simply reels her into a heated discussion or escalates into a fight.

How and why does this happen? Maybe it is a way for the one casting the worm (so to speak) to release pent up anger or get an adrenalin rush from a fight. It is important to remember that frequently baiting has very little to do with you and much more to do with the person doing the baiting. Their need to get what they want—in the form of getting your attention, your money, your time, or whatever else they may be demanding—is their need and desire. It is not your need, and it may not be in your best interest to respond. It is important to maintain a clear understanding of your own needs and keep in mind that engaging in someone else's demands is a choice. It is especially important to remember that you have the right and responsibility to choose how you will respond to their demands.

If and when someone starts baiting and attempts to escalate a conversation into a fight, another phrase that is useful is *"I'm not going to participate in this today."* Declining to participate in a provocative conversation means that you are respectfully but firmly *disengaging* from further involvement in the discussion. It sends a clear, concise message and establishes important boundaries. This is particularly helpful if someone is saying things that are rude and inappropriate. It also works if someone is trying to get you into a conversation about an emotional topic such as politics or religion and you already know that you strongly disagree. Instead of trying to change the other person, simply disengage and stop participating in the discussion.

Telling someone that you are choosing not to participate is a way of disengaging from further discussion. Disengagement is helpful because it makes the conversation less personal and emotional. It helps you detach from emotional involvement with the issue at hand and take a neutral position.

De-Escalating

Even when we use skills to disengage from conversations or situations that may bait us, we may still find ourselves feeling out of control and getting angry. If you are in a conversation that might be getting heated, it is important to take a step back and consider what you can do to de-escalate the situation. Maintaining both integrity and respect for yourself and the other person is important. You are entitled to disagree, and do not have to justify your thoughts or feelings. At the same time, exhibiting calm, respectful behavior to the other person can help both of you "win."

Naturally, when people have a conversation, there is a tendency to match each other in terms of tone, body language, and emotions. If one laughs, the other also smiles or laughs, if one is worried, the other may communicate that as well. Remember the mirror neurons in the brain? You can de-escalate a fight by doing precisely the opposite of the other person. For example, if someone is escalating emotionally, you can sit down calmly, show concern, and keep the focus on the person who is upset. The person will most likely also sit down, calm down, and lower his or her voice.

It's also helpful to choose words that are not personal, but rather cooperative. Instead of saying, "But you promised that you would . . ." you might try "We had an agreement that . . ." or "The understanding was . . . ." Try to think of the situation as something the two of you can face together, rather than a battle *against* each other.

Finally, your greatest ally in "winning" when dealing with difficult discussions is your empathy for the other person. Try to put yourself in his or her shoes, and see his or her point of view. You may not agree with what is being said, but at least you can understand where the other person is coming from. Letting that person know that you acknowledge his or her feelings and desires can work wonders in de-escalating difficult discussions. Remember the box where one person saw a blue rectangle and the other person saw a red square? Both perceptions are accurate but neither saw the whole picture. This can be very helpful to remember when trying to understand and resolve conflicts.

Tips for handling anger in communication:

1. When you notice yourself heating up, cool down with a *cleansing breath.*
2. If it's too hot, remove yourself and say, "I really want to have a discussion about this but let's take a break and talk later " (figure out a time a place).
3. Figure out why you are so upset—not only because of what someone said or did, but because of what it means to you. What is being triggered inside of you?
4. Practice seeing the problem from multiple points of view; seek to understand and then to be understood.
5. Focus on the immediate issue without saying slanderous things or shifting the focus to other issues.
6. If someone else is getting upset, sit down and calmly say, "I really want to hear what you are saying. Can we talk about it?" If the person calms down, then you can have a conversation. If the person escalates, then disengage and communicate that you will not participate until he or she is calm. You are allowed to hold boundaries!

Scenario 3: De-Escalating an Angry Person or Volatile Situation

In this exercise, participants will practice all the communication skills learned thus far. To practice dealing with someone who is baiting, escalating, or looking to get a reaction or rise out of you, role play a confrontational, irritating, or baiting interaction. The antagonist's role is to bait the person into an argument. She may cast a "hook" or simple make requests. Protagonists can use calm body language, tone, and empathy to communicate concern. The protagonist can choose not to take the bait by not responding to the potential hook. However, it may also be appropriate to disengage from the interaction. Protagonists can also use "Let me think about it," "I'm not going to participate in this today," and the broken record technique.

Again, set up the therapeutic stage, making it clear that the antagonist is only playing a role. The audience comments on what the protagonist did well and may provide any other feedback. After the scene the protagonist chooses someone from the audience to become the next antagonist and the former one becomes the protagonist. The facilitator manages the beginning and end of the scenes.

Never cut what you can untie.
—Joseph Joubert

CHAPTER 11 SUMMARY POINTS

■ What is effective communication? Communication that is received in the way it was intended.

■ It takes both a good toss and a good catch to complete a successful transmission of communication.

■ There are four key facets of communication: words, tone, emphasis, and body language.

■ There are three styles of communication: passive, assertive, and aggressive. How can each be adaptive?

■ The five magic words when someone makes a request of you and you are not sure how to respond are: *"Let me think about it."*

■ What can you say if someone is irritating you, pushing your buttons, or fishing for a fight? "I'm not going to participate in this." This is an opportunity to disengage from the conversation.

■ What is the *broken record* technique? Saying the same thing over and over.

■ Both the *foot-in-the-door* and *door-in-the-face* strategies are ways to manipulate someone to agree to something he or she might not otherwise agree to. Foot-in-the-door is getting someone to agree to something and then adding on just one more thing. Door-in-the-face is a big request followed by a smaller request. The person may feel more likely to do the small request because he or she declined the big one.

■ Empathy and understanding are key to good negotiation skills, leading to win–win outcomes.

Meaning, Purpose, and Joy

12

The real voyage of discovery consists of not in seeking new landscapes but in having new eyes.

—*Marcel Proust*

- *Opening exercises: Trust revisited*
  (Day 1: Trust walk, Day 2: Optional morning activities: Fill in the scene or hot potato)
- *Closing exercises: Who are you?*
  (Day 1: Who are you? Day 2: Mindful awareness)

Throughout the process of healing you have learned that you are not simply your trauma, but a complex amazing human being who has experienced and survived traumatic events. You might have discovered that there are many facets of traumatic events and now you can see them in their proper context. You may have realized that it is not worth holding onto the negativity because it keeps you from moving forward and enjoying your life. *The question is, how do you want to spend the rest of your precious life?*

DEFINING YOUR LIFE

While we are still always ourselves, we have choices to make each day as we go forward. We are able to identify what we want to have in our lives, and the things that we can let go of. We can consider the things that give us meaning and purpose, and the things that are a burden or not worth putting our energies into. If you have the possibility and responsibility to actively create your life, then who do you choose to be and what do you choose to do?

Although you may learn from experiences, you are not your experiences. Experiences may influence your thoughts and feelings, but your experiences do not define who you are. This distinction is key to understanding the way you define yourself in relation to your history of traumatic experiences. People tend to express themselves in absolute "states of being"—such as "I am stressed!" or "I am angry!" In reality, however, we experience many different states, and at any given time we are simply having a temporary experience (e.g., "I am having stress," "I am feeling angry"). Like water flowing through a hose, feelings are temporary states and they come and they go.

The following is a humorous conversation between two swans, Norma and Newman, adapted from a children's book, *Norma and Newman* (Katz & Katz, in press). It illustrates the fusion between identity and fleeting experiences.

> *Norma: Hi, I'm cold.*
> *Newman: Hi, Cold!*
> *Norma: No, I'm cold! Can you get me a blanket?*

In this conversation, there is a fusion between feelings and experiences with one's identity. In other words, people have life experiences but *they are not these experiences*. Similarly, you are not trauma; it is something that occurred and you survived. Now you are learning how to move through it and allow the experience to be an experience from your past. Similarly, you are not triggers and current upsets either. They are also experiences that do not have to define you or limit the rest of your life.

Washing Machine

Imagine you are a set of clothes inside a washing machine going around and around, getting mixed up with the soap and water. At some level you know you are being washed but you can't really make sense of the situation, can't control it, and can only do your best to survive. It is chaos and uncertainty. This is what it is like when you become your trauma. Life is a series of tumble and spin cycles!

Now imagine you are outside of the washing machine, watching the clothes go around. When you step out of the machine, you can see there is a beginning and end to the cycle, and the clothes are going to be fine, and even though you can see that it is chaos in there, you are not caught up in it. You are calm. You can watch the clothes and not become the clothes. This is what it is like when you can observe yourself going through a trauma-related event (e.g., trigger, nightmare, panic attack, disappointment, betrayal, or upset) without getting caught up in it. The tumbles happen and you know you will get through them without escalating or getting stuck or lost in them.

Life is so much more than surviving tumbles . . . just let them pass and focus on what you really want in life. You have the freedom and power to create good things for you!

Who Are You?

"Who are you?" asked the Caterpillar in Lewis Carroll's *Alice in Wonderland*. Alice replied that she is Alice of course. The Caterpillar asked again, "But WHO are you?" And so now *you* are being asked, "WHO are you?" Some people may think they are a role such as daughter, mother, or partner. Some people may think they are their preferences such as what they like or dislike. Others may think they are a member of a group such as their race, religion, or nationality. The truth is you may be all of these things and many more. In this class, let's consider that "you are who you say you are." You get to define you, not your past, not your trauma, not your family, not the military. These may be experiences that you have had, but you and only you can define yourself.

Imagine if someone says he is worthless—how do you think that person will act, respond to others, and interact with whatever circumstances arise? Probably not well and most likely consistent with someone who is "worthless." However, if that very same person, without changing anything about him, declares that he is a valuable human being, or funny, or well-liked, how do you think he would react? How would others react to him? People generate a chain of responses by the way they think about themselves.

So, who are you? You are who you say you are . . . and that is entirely up to you! Challenge yourself to think outside of the box on this one—don't hold back.

Writing exercise: **Who are you?** (You can be as creative as you would like with this exercise, maybe include special qualities about you, your character, talents, dreams, values, etc. You get to define you!)

_____

_____

_____

_____

_____

_____

_____

_____

POSSIBILITIES

Before defining values, purpose, and goals, it is important to acknowledge that your life is full of possibilities. This goes back to the discussion about being a "vector" and living your future from your past (i.e., experiencing more of the same) versus being a "point" and living fully present in this moment (i.e., where your future is what you create). Yes, the trauma happened, but you do not have to be a vector, you can be a point—right now, with all the possible directions and choices available to you.

From this perspective, you are a participant in the creation of your life. This means that your experience is a combination of what you, others, and circumstances bring to the moment. In other words, your attitude, energy, expectations, and behavior influence those around you just like things around you can influence you. Sometimes circumstances or other people can take control of the situation, but you always have a choice on how you are going to participate in the experience. If you realize there are many possibilities for what you want to create and how you want to experience life, you can own your own power and ability to influence your future.

Think about that for a moment. What do you want to create? By defining your values, purpose, and goals you will be more intentional about creating the future you desire.

> **If we did the things we are capable of, we would astound ourselves.**
> —*Thomas Edison*

CLARIFYING VALUES

You matter. With increased awareness comes an increased ability to find meaning and make a contribution to the things you believe are important. To clarify the things that you value, it can be helpful to begin with a writing exercise that starts "I value. . . ." For example: "I value spreading peace and compassion," or "I value a strong relationship with my family," or "I value preserving the environment." Whether they are close to home or on a global scale, it is helpful to identify the things that you feel are important—so you can live your life according to what you value. Your values can serve as an anchor to keep you on your chosen path. Does a decision, action, or communication fit with your values?

Values as Your GPS for Life

Remember the days before having a global positioning system (GPS) when driving? It was so easy to get lost, not know which direction to turn, and be completely oblivious to factors such as traffic, detours, and speed limits.

But now we have the technology to type in an address and the GPS tells us where to go. The GPS is not the car or the driver—it cannot make decisions for you (although some of them can be quite insistent!). It is merely a guide or a road map. If you make a different turn, your GPS will let you know that your driving is not consistent with the destination that you desire. And when you follow your GPS, the drive can be a lot less stressful. Similarly, your values are like your life GPS. You can set a destination of what is important to you—where you want to go in life. Decisions that are inconsistent with your values don't feel good and you will know that they are not the direction that you desire. Having a values-based GPS can be a comforting guide to keep you on track and move you toward your goals and destination.

Defining Your Values

What is important to you? What do you hold as an important value? (Some examples are honor, truth, loyalty, service to others, beauty, compassion, honesty, friendship, strength, and creativity.)

I value _____

I value _____

I value _____

I value _____

I value _____

I value _____

I value _____

I value _____

Now look at your list. What are your top three values? Circle what you value the most. The clearer you are with knowing who you are and choosing what matters to you most, the easier it is to act in ways consistent with what matters most to you. When you act in ways that are consistent with your values, you are behaving with integrity. When you have integrity, you build self-esteem and trust with others because they see you as someone who acts in ways consistent with your values. However, don't assume other people have the same values as you do. It can be frustrating when others don't act in ways that you think they should, but they are operating under a different set of assumptions. Remember their "book of the way life should be" may be different from yours.

How do your values influence your decisions? Think of a situation—how might your values influence your behavior?

_____

_____

> Your vision will become clear only when you can look into your own heart. Who looks outside, dreams; who looks inside, awakens.
> —*Carl Jung*

PURPOSE

Purpose, although related to how you define yourself, and what you value, is distinct. A purpose is feeling that you are a contribution to something. It may be a contribution to others, knowledge, a profession, or other activity. Being a contribution to something greater than yourself will, by definition, give you a sense of purpose. Purpose is like having a goal or something you are working toward. You might have heard the saying, "Keep your eye on the prize." This means keep your end-point or goal in mind to help you stay motivated. For example, if your goal is to finish a marathon race, then reminding yourself of your "prize" may keep you going, staying on your training schedule, and running just one more mile when you feel tired and want to give up. Purpose helps you *focus* your efforts and keeps you on track.

Purpose can also give you *strength* and the ability to overcome obstacles such as unfortunate circumstances or negativity. Purpose keeps you going because you know you are working for something important.

Purpose also gives your efforts *meaning*. When you have something to invest your time and effort toward, it makes you feel good and increases the meaning and value of your life.

PURPOSE → FOCUS, STRENGTH, AND MEANING

Let's discuss some examples of purpose. Purpose can be many different things. Purpose can be being creative, being athletic, or excelling in your chosen field. It can be helping raise a family, contributing to an important cause, or making a difference to others. However, the bigger your purpose, the more it will give you focus, strength, and meaning.

A single goal can give you focus, strength, and meaning, but it will only be temporary. If you can link the goal to an even bigger goal, then that bigger goal elevates the smaller one to an even higher purpose. The higher your goal, the bigger your purpose. For example, passing one test in a nutrition class is a goal unto itself, but passing the test may be part of a bigger goal of passing the class, which is part of a bigger goal of earning a degree in nursing, which is part of a bigger goal of securing a job, which is part of a bigger goal of growing a career in nursing, which is part of a bigger goal of helping children with chronic illness, which is part of a bigger goal of being a "contribution to support children and their families to provide excellent health care, instilling hope and healing."

What is your purpose? What would make your life as meaningful as possible? What do you think is worth fighting for, or working for? What gives you a sense of energy, enthusiasm, and passion? What do you really care about? Think as big as you can!

_____

_____

_____

_____

Once you define your purpose, the smaller goals will align themselves to build toward your purpose. **Given your purpose . . . what goals would you like to set?**

Immediate goals

_____

_____

Short-term goals

_____

_____

Medium-term goals

_____

_____

Long-term goals

_____

_____

Acting in Ways That Are Consistent With Your Values and Purpose

In this exercise, think of a challenging situation. How would you like to respond? Ask yourself the following four questions.

1. What do I want to create in this interaction?

_____

_____

2. How can I behave that will be consistent with what I want to create?

_____

_____

3. What emotions do I want to feel as I approach the situation?

_____

_____

4. Then act as if this is true and project *this* reality into your future.

_____

_____

Perhaps the first part of creating meaning and purpose is to continually enhance self-esteem and self-compassion. How do we do this? For one thing, at the end of each day, we can note at least one thing that we did right—the good decisions we made, the considerate actions we took, the problems we solved—that made a contribution to our own lives and those of other people. We can take stock of the ways we might have responded to a situation in the past that were unhelpful and/or unhealthy, and make a mental note of the ways we are now responding differently.

We can treat ourselves with kindness—by taking care of ourselves emotionally, physically, and spiritually. We can understand that sometimes we may return to sad or bad feelings related to our trauma, and remind ourselves that feelings flow through us like water through a hose and will eventually pass. New positive experiences will help weaken old associations and build new neural pathways. We can consciously cultivate friendships and communities that are uplifting. And we can know that as our healing continues we cannot but help to impact others in a positive way as we grow stronger.

CONTRIBUTION

If you have the possibility and responsibility to actively create your life, then who do you choose to be? If you are a lone leaf existing solely for the purpose of yourself, then how meaningful is the purpose of your life? However, if you are a lone leaf that is a contribution to a tree, then your life becomes very meaningful and purposeful as it supports the tree. If the tree is a contribution to the planet's oxygen; to the stability of the earth; to providing shade, fruit, or a nesting space for birds, then the leaf is also a contribution to these purposes. The lone leaf is now a contribution to a much bigger purpose than he or she could achieve alone. We can all be contributions to the health and well-being of others and to the survival of our planet. How does it feel to be a contribution to the planet?

Being a Contribution

Start your sentence with the phrase, "I am a contribution to. . . ."
Some examples are:

"I am a contribution to peace on the planet."
"I am a contribution to spreading understanding and compassion."
"I am a contribution to everyone I meet."

Notice that the scope of these contributions is broad. The idea is to have "being a contribution" as part of your identity that is lived daily and in a multitude of relationships. You can also be a contribution to many purposes.

For example: "I am a contribution to the planet by raising two beautiful loving sons. I teach my sons about kindness and tolerance. I see them lovingly interact with our friends and I feel that I am contributing to the well-being of others."

"I am a contribution to everyone I see in my environment. I contribute by smiling, asking about their day, and by being a respectful, concerned citizen."

"I am a contribution to the preservation of the natural environment. I contribute by recycling my garbage, by donating to environmental agencies, and by picking up litter when I see it in my path."

What are you a contribution to?

I am a contribution to_____

_____

I am also a contribution to _____

_____

_____

I am also a contribution to _____

_____

_____

Imagining the Effects of Your Contribution

Imagine that your contribution leads to a positive ripple effect—affecting your health, attitude, and well-being. Imagine your contribution leads to positive feelings in others, spreading to those closest to you and then to those all around you. Imagine that they carry forth your positive influence and it spreads. Each word and each event may be rather small, but if you tallied up how many words or actions you say or do over a day, a week, or your lifetime, then you can see that you do have an impact on the collective whole.

Who do you want to be in the world?

FUTURE SELF

Writing exercise: Write about your future self. What activities and ways of being could sustain you, give you energy, and bring you joy? What would you like to envision for your future?

_____

_____

_____

_____

_____

_____

_____

_____

_____

_____

_____

_____

FINDING JOY

While anger and fear are toxic, causing a host of problems, joy is an elixir. It elevates mood, decreases stress, and improves relationships. People experiencing joy are more relaxed physically, able to concentrate better, and may even have better eyesight than others! However, with busy and stressful lives, people sometimes forget how to celebrate life and experience joy. Joy can be quiet or boisterous. It may be planned, through scheduling activities that bring pleasure and happiness, or it can be spontaneous. Part of the experience of joy is noticing when it occurs, and also offering yourself plenty of opportunities for it.

What brings you joy? What opens up your social, emotional, and spiritual channels? It might come from connecting to others, prayer, singing, or communal activities. It might come from doing a hobby, going to new places, or helping others. Joy can be found in playing with children, who are naturally spontaneous, or in meditation and cultivating mindfulness. It can come from being in nature (mountains, beaches, or in a park), or through enjoyment of art or other activities of creative self-expression. Joy can come through dancing or running or playing sports. Joy can be found in so many things—the key is finding the opportunities for joy in your own life.

> What I know for sure is that you feel real JOY in direct proportion to how connected you are to living your truth.
> —*Oprah Winfrey*

What Brings You Joy?

What do you think are some benefits of having joy in your life? Joy is very good for our physical, mental, and emotional health. It supports the immune system, elevates mood, decreases stress, and improves relationships. Even if you have shut yourself off from feelings of joy, the potential is still inside of you. Do you remember ever having joy? If not, then what do you think would open up that feeling for you now?

1. **What brings you joy (makes you smile, feel good, feel happy)?**

_____

_____

_____

2. **What are three things you would like to try, at least once?**

_____

_____

_____

3. Name three things you used to do that you enjoyed.

_____

_____

_____

4. Name three of your dream vacations.

_____

_____

_____

5. If you had unlimited funds, time, and ability what would like to do?

_____

_____

_____

Review the answers that you gave in this section. Do you notice any themes? What parts can you incorporate into your life? For example, Susan fantasizes about being an artist and living in Italy. What could she do to incorporate some of this fantasy into her reality? She can take an art class, and she can carry a sketch pad with her in her car or a small one in her purse. She may find that when she is somewhere waiting, she could be sketching. She may want to plan a trip to Italy or just go to "Little Italy" in a nearby city, go to an Italian restaurant, take a class on Italian classical art, learn the language, or. . . . As you can see, there are many ways Susan can incorporate part of this fantasy into her life. There are ways to live parts of many lives in this one lifetime.

Using the information you wrote on the previous page, what can you do to experience more joy in your daily life? Name five concrete things you can do to incorporate more joy into your life.

1. _____

2. _____

3. _____

4. _____

5. _____

Incorporate moments of joy into each day.
It's those little things, those precious moments that bring happiness to life!

FINAL IMAGERY EXERCISE

Start with two to three *signal breaths*. Create an image of yourself—the person who you say you are. Imagine yourself walking on a sidewalk. How do you look? How do you walk? Imagine what you are wearing and how you are moving. You know your values and what is possible for you. You know your purpose and your goals. Imagine yourself being the you who you choose to be. How does it feel? Keep this image with you to remind you of this amazing and wonderful you! Know that you can always come back to this image. You may want to keep this image in your heart or somewhere you can access it easily again. End with two to three *cleansing breaths*.

How about trying some of the following?

Walk barefoot	Eat with your hands	Make a silly face
Go to a concert	Laugh out loud	Sing or dance
Ride a bike	Paint your toes a wild color	Go to a batting cage
Go on a hike	Play an instrument	Take pictures
Get a massage	Buy yourself a present	Take a day off from work
Complete a project	Write a poem	Wear a hat or long scarf
Buy/pick fresh flowers	Light a candle	Eat something new
Hit a bucket of golf balls	Blow soap bubbles	Spend a day at the spa
Snuggle up and read a book	Draw with crayons	Go to a sporting event
Change your hair	Wiggle your hips	Take a bubble bath
Paint/draw/sew/crochet	Plant flowers/vegetables	Walk by the beach
Go to a lecture	Take a class	Browse at a bookstore
Join a group/club	Walk in a mall	Volunteer
Visit an art museum	Walk through a park	Organize your closet
Go to a movie	Go to the aquarium	Play a game (cards, checkers)
Play Frisbee	Sightsee	Play a sport

What else would you like to do?

_____

_____

Congratulations! This is the conclusion of this course.

Do you notice any changes? If so, how have you changed?

_____

What made the biggest impact for you?

_____

What was the most difficult part?

_____

What was the most meaningful part?

_____

Name three new skills you have learned in this course.

1. _____

2. _____

3. _____

CHAPTER 12 SUMMARY POINTS

- Who are you? What is your identity? How would you define you? You get to define you, not your past, your family, your trauma, the military, or other people. So who do you say you are?
- What do you want to create in your life? What do you value? Living consistent with your values is living with integrity.
- Purpose helps you focus your efforts and keeps you on track. Purpose can also give you strength and the ability to overcome obstacles such as unfortunate circumstances or negativity. Purpose keeps you going because you know you are working for something important.
- Purpose also gives your efforts meaning. When you have something to invest your time and effort toward, it makes you feel good and increases the meaning and value of your life.
- What are your immediate, short-term, and long-term goals? Are these consistent with your values and purpose?
- What brings you joy? Are there things in the past that you used to enjoy? How about things you would like to do but have never had the chance or time to do? What would bring more happiness to you in your life?

Remember your image of yourself being your best you!

Final Thoughts

This is the end of our *Warrior Renew* journey together. But before you go, I want to congratulate you! You confronted your fears and addressed your feelings. (Remember the taped-up box of feelings?) I know it took a lot of effort to show up and participate. May you reap the rewards of your efforts and find your life growing in wonderful ways. Truly my greatest wish is for you to thrive.

Do you remember when you first started? How you felt, the concerns you had, and the heavy bags you were carrying? How do they feel now? I hope they are a little lighter.Know that your healing may be a process that continues to unfold. If you are moving in a new direction, even slightly, then your life will change. You may feel the effects of the program months, or even years, from now. I also want to reassure you that if you find old patterns reemerging, relationships having upsets, and life not going smoothly, it is only temporary. When you are lost, what will you do? Consult your values-based GPS for directions to get back on your path . . . then something may remind you to breathe, use COPE, practice a moment of mindfulness, realize it's your hologram, or put blame where blame is due. When someone asks you for a favor you might just say, "Let me think about it!" The knowledge will be there when you need it. Most importantly, it is my hope that *Warrior Renew* inspires you to go forth and live the life that you desire. I wish you the very, very best.

—*Lori S. Katz, PhD*

Opening Exercises

Exercises with an asterisk (*) have been adapted from the Augustus Boal (1999) book of games for actors and non-actors. Other games were adapted from popular childhood games and the author's imagination. Starting in Week 3 (Chapter 2), and all sessions thereafter, group begins with everyone standing in a circle. The facilitator leads the group: "Take in a deep breath while raising your arms above your head, stretch . . . feel the expansion all the way through your fingertips . . . and then exhale while bringing the arms down." The goal is to stretch and breathe. This can be augmented with a few more gentle stretches (or shakes and wiggles) that suit the group. Then the group engages in one of the following games.

ORIENTATION: GROUP INTRODUCTIONS

1. *Introductions, Day 1.* This is the first meeting for everyone in the group. It can be a little awkward and people may have mixed feelings about being in a group. It is suggested that each person say their name, branch of service, what they hope to gain from the course, and their favorite flavor of ice cream.

2. *Introductions, Day 2.* On the second day of group, everyone is asked to share why they joined the military and then pick a positive adjective that starts with the first letter of their first name, such as Merry Molly, Creative Chris, Terrific Tina, or Ravishing Ruth. This is designed as an easy and fun way to help everyone remember the group members' names.

CHAPTER 1: NAMES AND BUILDING SAFETY

3. *Adjective name memory game.* On the first day of this chapter, begin with the following game. This game helps people remember the names of everyone in the class. It is also designed to be a little challenging while allowing the group to be supportive of each other. Everyone sits in a circle. The first person in the circle says his or her adjective and name pair (e.g., Serious Sam). The next person to the right says the first person's adjective and name then adds his or her own (Serious Sam, Bouncing Bob). The next person to the right says the first person's name, then second person's name and then adds his or her own name. Continue around the circle, each time adding one more person's name. The last person has to remember everyone's adjective and name pair. Congratulate the group at the end.

4. *Concentration name game.* On the second day of this chapter, begin with the following game. This game is a little more challenging as it requires coordination of movement, rhythm, and remembering names! The added dimensions of this game facilitate memory, increase group cohesion, and help participants heighten their awareness. First the group gets a rhythm going—one pat on the knees, one clap, and two snaps (e.g., right hand snap, then left hand snap). The beat is an even 1-2-3-4. Then the leader says her name on the two snaps (e.g., Artistic Ann) and then on the next two snaps, says someone else's name (e.g., Jump'n Jane). Then Jump'n Jane says her name on the two snaps and sends it to someone else (e.g., Happy Helen) until everyone has a chance to receive and send a name. Everyone applauds and says, "Good job!" This may sound easy but it can be challenging! If the person speaking loses his or her rhythm, do not stop—the group keeps the rhythm going so it stays on beat. The group can be helpful, supportive, and enjoy the laughter.

CHAPTER 2: MOVEMENT AND BUILDING SAFETY

5. *Water molecule.* On the first day of this chapter, begin with the following game. Clear the space of tables and chairs as best as possible. After breathing and stretching, start the *water molecule* exercise. Everyone is instructed to randomly walk around the room. The instructor says, "Randomly walk around the room, filling every space," and continues until everyone seems comfortable simply moving about. Then the instructor says, "Now imagine we are one big water molecule where everyone is a moving atom. . . . Now imagine the water molecule has been put in a pot on a stove and it is starting to heat up! As it gets warmer everyone moves faster . . . until it is boiling, boiling . . . hot! Then the water molecule comes off of the stove, coming back to room temperature—moving at a room temperature pace. . . ." Then the facilitator says, "Imagine the water molecule is put into the freezer, and it slowly starts to cool down, moving slower and slower as it gets colder and colder . . . until it is almost completely frozen but still moving ever so slightly! Until it is frozen solid." Then the facilitator says, "Okay, imagine the water molecule comes back to room temperature, slowly thawing." If everyone is still enjoying the exercise, and there is time, it can continue to include the following: "And now the molecule has become a drop of soda pop! Fizzing, bubbling, all around the room. . . . Come back to room temperature." Everyone applauds and says, "Good job!"

6. *Groupings.** On the second day of this chapter, after breathing and stretching, everyone does a quick giant *water molecule* by randomly walking around the room. The facilitator says, "Freeze!" While participants are frozen they are given instructions for the next activity. Participants are asked not to say anything but to group themselves according to eye color. Again, while remaining in silence they are then asked to group themselves into one triangle and one circle. The third grouping is standing in a line in alphabetical order by the letter of their first name (again without saying anything!). An additional optional grouping, if there is time, would be to stand in line by the month of their birthday in chronological order (i.e., January to December, skipping any months with no birthdays but still being in order).

CHAPTER 3: BUILDING TRUST

7. *Follow the hand.** On the first day of this chapter, after stretching and breathing, everyone does a quick giant *water molecule* by randomly walking around the room. The facilitator says, "Freeze!" then asks everyone to find a partner. One person is A and the other is B. One person is the leader and other the follower. The person leading lifts her hand and pretends it is a magnetic hand. Where she moves her palm the other person follows. Then switch roles.

8. *Mirrors.* On the second day of this chapter, after stretching and breathing, everyone does a quick giant *water molecule* by randomly walking around the room. The facilitator says, "Freeze!" then asks everyone to find a partner. One person is A and the other is B. One person is the leader and other the follower. In this game it is as if one person is looking into a mirror and the mirror mimics every move the person makes. The person who is leading moves his arms, legs, facial expression, and so on, and the other person follows. Then switch roles. Then have a round of "no leaders" with the pair continuing to mirror each other.

CHAPTER 4: BUILDING GROUP COHESION

9. *Pass the object.* On the first day of this chapter, after stretching and breathing, everyone remains standing in a circle. The leader starts by passing an imaginary object from one person to the other until it goes around the circle. Use objects such as a light feather, heavy bowling ball, tiny grain of rice, large box, and a fragile—very tall—wedding cake. This should be fun and imaginative.

10. *Group mirror.** On the second day of this chapter, after stretching and breathing, everyone does a quick giant *water molecule* by randomly walking around the room. The facilitator says, "Freeze!" and then asks everyone to find a partner. One person is A and the other is B. The dyads face each other, forming two lines of people so that all of the As are on the right and all the Bs are on the left. All the As are one group and the Bs another group, but everyone knows who their corresponding person is in the other group (the other half of the dyad). The As turn around while the Bs pose into a statue. Then the As turn around and look at the statues of the corresponding Bs for 5 seconds and "take a mental snapshot," then turn away. Those in the original statue poses disperse. Then the As turn around and replicate the Bs' poses. Each person recreates what their partner did. Then B can verify or correct the image. The groups switch roles.

CHAPTER 5: EXPRESSING WITH THE BODY

11. *Statues.** On the first day of this chapter, after stretching and breathing, everyone does a quick giant *water molecule* by randomly walking around the room. The facilitator says, "Freeze!" The class is asked to make a statue (using their bodies as if they were statues) of various emotions and concepts, for example: "grateful," "angry," "disappointment," "peace," "you after graduating from this course!" Randomly walk around the room between statues.

12. *Sculpting.** On the second day of this chapter, after stretching and breathing, everyone does a quick giant *water molecule* by randomly walking around the room. The facilitator says, "Freeze!" and then asks everyone to find a partner. One person is A and the other is B. Designate one as the artist and the other as clay. The artist is supposed to sculpt clay into a statue. Artists step back and look at their creations. Then trade. (Participants ask their partners for permission before touching or moving their bodies. If people feel uncomfortable, the artist can show or tell the clay what to do.)

CHAPTER 6: INTRODUCING SOUND

13. *Conductor.* On the first day of this chapter, everyone stands in a circle. Each person uses his or her voice to make a sound as if he or she were an instrument. The conductor leads the band, pointing to instruments to start or stop and get louder or softer. See what kind of rhythm the band can make. Take turns being the conductor.

14. *Circular rhythms.** On the second day of this chapter, begin with the following game. In this exercise, everyone sits in a chair in a circle. One person starts a sound (such as clapping on ones thighs) and continues to do it. The person to the right copies it, then the person to her right copies it, until everyone is doing the sound. When it gets to the original person, she continues to do it and the person to her right starts a new sound.

   Now there are two sounds going on, the original one and the new one. (People continue with the old sound until the person next to them changes.) Everyone continues to pass the new sound around the room until the person to the right of the original person gets it and changes it and passes it around the room. The game continues until everyone has had a chance to initiate a new sound.

CHAPTER 7: COMBINING MOVEMENT AND SOUND

15. *Four-person trains.** On the first day of this chapter, after stretching and breathing, everyone does a quick giant *water molecule* by randomly walking around the room. The facilitator says, "Freeze!" While participants are frozen they are given instructions for the next activity. Participants are grouped into fours. They stand in line as if they were a train. The first person makes a movement and sound and the rest of the train follows. The train walks around the room doing the movement and sound. Then the facilitator says, "Switch," and the first person goes to the end of the train. The new leader does the original movement and sound and adds a new one. Continue until everyone has a chance to be a leader (and doing four movements and sounds!).

16. *Machine.* On the second day of this chapter, begin with the following game. For this exercise, everyone stands in a circle (after stretching) and one person goes in the middle and makes a sound and does an action (movement). Then someone joins her and makes a sound and action in a complementary rhythmic fashion. One by one, everyone adds to the group in the middle. This is one giant machine moving and making sounds together. Then the facilitator asks the machine to slow down and speed up, and act as if it is sad and then happy. End with a round of applause for the group!

CHAPTER 8: EXPLORING POWER

17. *Game of power.** On the first day of this chapter, everyone gets a chair and stands behind it in a circle. The task is to see who can make his or her chair the most powerful chair in the room. Each chair is placed one at a time to see if that chair could be more powerful than the last one placed in the room. Then discuss what the exercise meant to participants. There are different types of power: (1) power ascribed to a position such as an authority figure, (2) power inherited by birth, (3) power of controlling or obtaining resources, and so on. Can you think of other forms of power? In this class, we explore the idea of "authentic power." All the other forms of power are actually weak because they can be taken away or lost—they are external and, therefore, people have a level of fear of losing them. Only authentic power is real power—it is within and can never be diminished or taken away. Even if your body is trapped, your mind and spirit can always be free. Your authentic power is knowing that the truth of what is inside of you is always with you—and this gives you your internal strength.

18. *Guess the leader.** On the second day of this chapter, everyone sits in a circle. One person goes out of the room. Among those remaining, one person is designated as leader. He or she starts a movement such as clapping. Everyone in the circle follows the leader and continues to do so until he or she changes the action (tapping her thighs or snapping) and then everyone follows that action. The person outside comes in and watches the group and tries to guess who the leader is. Participants should not look directly at the leader but should try to change together as quickly as possible!

CHAPTER 9: COMMUNITY

19. *Rain.* On the first day of this chapter, everyone sits in a tight circle. The facilitator says, "We're going to make rain!" The facilitator starts by rubbing his or her hands together and passing it around the room so that the person to the right does whatever the person to the left is doing. Once everyone is rubbing their hands together, the facilitator starts with soft snapping and passes this around the room. (People continue to rub their hands until the person on their left is snapping.) Then, the facilitator passes around tapping on his or her thighs, then clapping, then louder clapping with foot stomping, until the group is making a thundering rainstorm, and then the facilitator tapers it down by just clapping, tapping his or her thighs, snapping, and finally hand rubbing until there is silence.

20. *Cupid*. On the second day of this chapter, everyone sits in a tight circle. The facilitator has small pieces of paper, one for each person. One piece has a heart on it and the rest have stars. Everyone is given a paper (discretely so nobody sees what is on them). The one with the heart is the cupid and tries to shoot people with the arrow of love by winking at them. The cupid tries to wink at everyone without being caught. Other people are tryçow who it is!" and correctly guesses the cupid the game is over. If he or she guesses wrong, then both of those people are out. Once someone is shot, then discretely he or she says, "Oh, I've been shot!" and is out of the game. The cupid tries to shoot everyone before getting caught!

CHAPTER 10: EXPLORING BALANCE

21. *Balance*. On the first day of this chapter, everyone stands in a circle. After stretching and breathing, everyone is asked to stand on their toes, keeping their balance and then down. Next, they are asked to stand on one foot and if possible on the toes of one foot (then change feet). The idea is to work on balance. It may be helpful to stare at one spot or to use one's arms for balance. People with disabilities may want to hold onto the back of a chair for support. Then everyone is asked to stand perfectly still with both feet on the ground, first with eyes open, then eyes closed. What does everyone notice? Is it possible to be perfectly still? What does this exercise illustrate about balance?

22. *Peruvian ball passing*.* On the second day of this chapter, after stretching and breathing, everyone does a quick giant *water molecule* by randomly walking around the room. The facilitator says, "Freeze!" and then asks everyone to find a partner. One person is A and the other is B. Each person plays with an imaginary ball (basketball, tennis ball, volleyball, etc.). After playing with the ball, the facilitator asks the partners to switch balls. After playing with their new ball, they are asked to find a new partner. Again they switch balls. Continue until the balls have been switched three times. Then everyone goes into one big circle, playing with their most recent ball, and everyone tries to find their original ball!

CHAPTER 11: INTERACTIVE COMMUNICATION EXERCISES

23. **& 24.** *Vocal warm-up exercises*. This week covers communication skills, which includes interactive exercises. So for both days of this chapter, stand in a circle and stretch. Maybe add a few more stretches such as side to side or a gentle forward bend. Then practice vocal exercises that stage actors do to warm up their vocal chords and stretch their

mouths and jaws. The group repeats the following phrase three times, opening the jaw as far as is comfortable: "How now brown cow!" Another warm-up exercise is to repeat this phrase while clearly articulating: "The lips, the teeth, the tip of the tongue." Exaggerate the movements and try to "pop" the sounds. Do this before both of the classes this week. Then shake out the body or dance to warm up before class.

CHAPTER 12: TRUST REVISITED

25. *Trust walk.* On the first day of this chapter, after stretching and breathing, everyone does a quick giant *water molecule* by randomly walking around the room. The facilitator says, "Freeze!" and then asks everyone to find a partner. One person is A and the other is B. One person will guide the other person, who has his or her eyes closed or is blindfolded, around the room. The guide and the follower only connect by touching the tips of one index finger. With only this bit of information, the leader guides the person forward, backward, faster, or slower. If participants are comfortable, they can get creative! After a few minutes, the participants switch roles. Discuss what this was like. Would participants have been able to do this in the beginning of the program? Discuss how have they changed.

26. *Optional morning activities.* On the second day of the chapter, participants have a choice to simply stretch and breathe or do one of the optional exercises below.

    *Fill in the scene.** Everyone stands in a circle. One person goes into the middle of the circle and starts an action such as brushing his teeth. One by one, others join the scene and help define it. For example, one person may be the sink, a towel, or a mirror!

    Hot potato. Everyone sits in a circle and passes an object around the circle to music. When the music stops, the person with the object is out. Continue until one person remains (without the object!).

REVIEW WEEK

There are no morning exercises this week, but class can begin with standing in a circle, breathing and stretching.

Appendix B

Closing Exercises

Closing exercises are intended to be relaxing and fun. Especially after an emotionally intense group, closing exercises help release tension and end the session with everyone feeling calm. It is optional to end any class with a relaxation sandwich—start with two *signal breaths*, do a relaxation exercise such as body scan or mindful awareness, and end with two *cleansing breaths*.

ORIENTATION

There is no closing exercise this week. Classes this week are designed to prepare participants for the *Warrior Renew* program. Next week begins the full program.

CHAPTER 1: SIGNAL AND CLEANSING BREATHS

See end of Chapter 1 for a detailed explanation of *signal* and *cleansing breaths*.

1. *Signal breath.* At the end of class on the first day of this chapter, participants learn the *signal breath*, which is a deep breath in through the nose, hold it at the top for five counts, and then slowly release. One reason it is called a *signal breath* is that, like at a stop signal, it requires you to stop before moving forward. The group practices this three times, pausing in between to feel the relaxation.

2. *Cleansing breath and relaxation sandwich.* At the end of the second day of this chapter, participants learn the *cleansing breath*, which is a deep breath in through the nose (without holding it) and out through the mouth with a sigh. The sigh increases the benefits of this breath. Try it with and without the sigh to see the difference. The group practices this three times, pausing in between to feel the relaxation.

Then practice the *relaxation sandwich*. The "bread" of the sandwich is the two breaths (*signal* and *cleansing*). Any relaxation exercise is the filling. Start with two *signal breaths*, experience a relaxing period of silence focusing on being present, feeling the sensations of the breath, and feeling your feet on the floor and your back in the chair. Then end with two *cleansing breaths*, exhaling completely with a good sigh.

CHAPTER 2: RELAXATION SKILLS

3. *Body scan and emotional scan*. At the end of class, participants learn the *body scan* and *emotional scan* sandwiched between the *signal breath* and the *cleansing breath*.

4. *Biofeedback machine and decoding your feelings*. At the end of the second day of this chapter, participants practice the *biofeedback machine* and the six-step *decoding your feelings* exercise (presented in Chapter 2), again sandwiched between the *signal breath* and *cleansing breath*.

CHAPTER 3: AROMATHERAPY

5. *Explore different scents*. At the end of the first class of Chapter 3, discuss different scents (which ones make you feel good). Use aroma products such as good-quality aromatherapy oils. Practice *signal breaths* and *cleansing breaths*. Choose one or two scents to share with the group (and no more than three in a room at a time). Use sparingly. End class with two *signal breaths*, body scan, and then two to three *cleansing breaths*. *Note:* Do not smell the bottle of aromatherapy oil, but rather place a drop of the oil in the palm of your hand. You don't want the bacteria from your nose (or everyone else's!) to get on the bottle.

6. *Make nightmare sachets*. At the end of the second day of this chapter, make nightmare sachets (see Chapter 3). This can be filled with potpourri, dried flowers, cloves, or scented soap shavings. Do not use oils, as they will seep through the material and become rancid. Nightmare sachets are a good tool to "get present" and clear negative thoughts and images from the mind. End class with two *signal breaths*, body scan, and then two to three *cleansing breaths*.

CHAPTER 4: GUIDED IMAGERY

At the end of class for both Day 1 and Day 2 of this chapter, the relaxation part will use "guided imagery." Start with two *signal breaths* followed by one of the imagery scripts and end with two to three *cleansing breaths*. The focus for this week is on feeling safe, relaxed, trusting, and calm on the inside. The facilitator can add supportive statements, background instrumental music, and/or aromatherapy. Other places may include a country road, waterfall, garden, or mountain scene. Each image should activate all of the senses (sights, sounds, smells, taste, and sensations).

7. *Tropical beach scene*. (Only use this if everyone is comfortable with a beach scene, otherwise substitute another nature scene that is "safe" for the group.)

"Feel yourself sitting in your chair, spine against the chair, arms resting comfortably in your lap. Feel your feet on the ground. Allow your breathing to deepen, slowing down, and exhale. Feel your shoulders soften . . . letting go of any tension in your neck and shoulders. Feel your forehead soften . . . and your jaw . . . just letting your body relax while we go on a mini-vacation to a beautiful tropical beach. Imagine it's a clear sunny day with a bright blue sky and turquoise-colored water. You can feel the warmth of the sun on your skin. You already feel more relaxed. You are lying under a palm tree on a plush towel on the soft white sand. Feel yourself lying on the sand . . . it has contoured to the shape of your body, like a big soft pillow beneath you. It feels very comfortable. You are completely supported and you breathe. . . . You can hear the sounds of the waves gently washing onto shore, back and forth, rhythmically. The sound is soothing. . . . Maybe there are a few seagulls calling in the distance. You take in a deep breath of the fresh air, smelling a hint of the seaweed in the air. You can almost taste a slight salty sensation in the back of your throat. It's so nice and clean and refreshing. Just let yourself feel relaxed by the beach. The sounds of the waves rock you back and forth ever so gently. You can completely relax and soften all the muscles in your body. Notice your breath . . . inhaling and exhaling. Notice the slight movement with each breath going in and out—like the waves going back and forth . . . ever so gently." If you have beach sounds, you can play this in the background. To end the scene: "Now take in a deep breath and exhale, knowing this relaxing scene is inside of you and you can visit here whenever you want. Again, take in a deep breath and exhale, bringing your awareness of sitting in the chair, your feet on the ground . . . and arms resting comfortably in your lap. Wiggle your fingers and toes and slowly open your eyes, stretching and yawning. . . ."

8. *Mountain waterfall*.

"Imagine being at a waterfall in the mountains. It is a beautiful sunny day and you can feel the warmth of the sun on your skin. The sky is a bright blue and you can see just one small white fluffy cloud in the distance. There are many pine trees and rocks. You can smell the fresh scent of pine in the air. You see one particular large grey rock that looks inviting. You climb on top and find a comfortable place to sit. The rock is warm and smooth, as it has been weathered over time. You have a perfect view of a magnificent waterfall. The water seems to endlessly flow and dances its way down over the rocks, playfully jumping and skipping and spraying up in the air. A light spray of the water comes your way. It is refreshing and cool on your skin. The constant rumble of the falling water is soothing. It is so peaceful being up in the mountains. The air is fresh and clear. You lie back and soak in this wonderful feeling. You are completely relaxed, refreshed, and feel inspired. Take in a deep breath and exhale completely."

CHAPTER 5: QUIET MUSIC AND INTRODUCTION TO MINDFUL AWARENESS

9. & 10. *Introduction to mindful awareness.* Mindful awareness is a practice of being in the present moment and not allowing your thoughts or attention to go elsewhere. If you notice your thoughts wandering into the past or future, or if you notice yourself thinking about anything in particular, gently redirect your attention to experiencing this moment. Some find it easier to learn mindfulness by having something to focus on, such as breathing or listening to music. This week will be about exploring the experience of mindfully listening to music.

Listen to music. At the end of class for both Day 1 and Day 2 of this chapter, everyone quietly listens to relaxing instrumental music (begin with two to three *signal breaths*, listen to the music, and end with two to three *cleansing breaths*). Participants are instructed to enjoy the music and stay present with their experience. If they notice negative or worrisome thoughts arising, they should just notice them and let them pass. The facilitator can say, "Bring your attention back to the music, back to being present. Imagine yourself opening to the now and allowing good things to come into your life. You are right here, enjoying this moment, this breath!" This can be practiced with eyes open or closed.

CHAPTER 6: MUSICAL BELLS AND CHIMES

11. & 12. *Singing bowl and chimes.* At the end of class for both Day 1 and Day 2 of this chapter, the relaxation exercise is to explore and play musical instruments such as a meditation bells, Tibetan singing bowls, or meditation chimes. If the facilitator has a special instrument, this can be demonstrated and then passed around the room for participants to play. This is an opportunity to explore listening with the body. These instruments each have unique vibrations. What does it sound like? What does it feel like? End with the following sequence: two *signal breaths*, the facilitator rings the bowl/chime 10 times, allowing the sounds to go to silence each time, and then two *cleansing breaths*.

CHAPTER 7: CHANTING AND TONING

The relaxation exercises at the end of class for both Day 1 and Day 2 of this chapter are about exploring the voice as an instrument through singing and chanting. One of the issues related to MST is closing the throat, staying in silence, and shutting down self-expression—which is related to one's power. Opening the throat and allowing yourself to make sounds helps in rebalancing this important system.

13. *Chanting CALM.* For chanting, everyone sits in a circle. First take a few deep breaths and then practice chanting the word *calm*. Take in a deep breath and slowly say, "C—A—L—M," extending the word (the "ah" sound) for the entire exhale. Repeat two more times. Sit quietly for a few minutes feeling the sensations. End with two *cleansing breaths*.

14. *Chanting vowels and "spaceship."* At the end of the second day of the chapter, everyone sits in a circle and practices chanting the vowels one at a time: A ("ay"), E ("ee"), I ("eye"), O ("oh"), and U ("you"). Start with two *signal breaths*. Then everyone takes in a deep breath and says the first vowel, "ay," for the whole exhale, as if singing and holding a note for as long as you can (comfortably). Do not talk in between chants. Focus on the chant. Then take a second inhale and chant the same vowel again. Chant each vowel *three times*, taking a breath and a brief moment of silence between each chant. This exercise helps open the throat and really clears the mind! See if your voices sound like the instruments you played last week. Do you feel the same vibrations inside and all around you? As the throat opens so does the power center that is located about 2 inches below the navel. This is an important exercise and participants should be able to feel the effects. Enjoy a few minutes of silence at the end of the exercise before doing the final *cleansing breaths*.

If the group is really enjoying chanting, you can add this extra piece after the vowel chanting. *Spaceship* is an exercise where the whole group starts with a low sound and increases the pitch to as high of a sound as they can go. Everyone uses their arms in connection with the sound, starting low with arms reaching down then scooping up the air, so by the end everyone raises their arms high up toward the ceiling. Everyone ends with a high "woop!" It sounds like this: (low) "OOOooooooooooooooooo . . . woop!" (high) and the arms follow. It might feel like the group is going up in a spaceship!

CHAPTER 8: EXPLORING POWER

15. *Power postures.* At the end of the class, participants explore the sensation of authentic internal power. Explore how it feels when you are in certain physical postures. The first position is standing at attention, shoulders back, arms pointing down, stomach tight, feet pushing down on the floor, and knees slightly bent. Head is lifted from the top but chin is parallel to the floor (not pointing up). In this posture, feel yourself grounded yet lifting upward. Feel your strength!

    The next position is standing with the knees slightly bent, spine straight, and pointing the fingers of the right hand upward (thumb toward the heart) and the fingers of the left hand downward (thumb away from the body), the left below the right. Hold the hands close to the body. And breathe, feeling the power of this position. If participants know the yoga poses "Warrior I" and "Warrior II" they can do these postures. If the class does not know these poses, they can use their bodies to make a statue to express "power," "warrior," and "self-confidence." Shake out the body in between poses. If participants want to sit quietly listening to a few minutes of music, this can be added. End with two *signal breaths*, body scan, mindful awareness, and two to three *cleansing breaths*.

16. *Walking like a tiger.* At the end of the second day of the chapter, we continue to explore the sensations of authentic power. When a tiger walks into a room, everyone knows to respect the tiger. The tiger does not need to show its teeth or roar; people just know that the tiger is a powerful animal that deserves respect. Similarly, you too can walk into a room as a powerful being. Imagine how you would walk if you were the embodiment of a tiger. Everyone stands and walks like a tiger, either in a circle or randomly in the room—feeling the quiet power within. Pay attention to your feet, legs, gut, shoulders, arms, face . . . how does it feel to walk as the powerful being that you are? Imagine you are a force to be reckoned with . . . and nobody and nothing can ever diminish the power within you. End with *signal breath* and mindful awareness, followed by two *cleansing breaths*. Great job!

CHAPTER 9: RELEASE AND MINDFUL AWARENESS

At the end of class for Day 1 is either *release* or *mindful awareness*. If the group opts not to do the releasing exercise, then mindfulness can be practiced on both days, with one day being "closed-eye awareness" and the next day "open-eyed awareness."

17. *Release (optional exercise for the end of the first day of the chapter).* In this exercise, sit closely in a circle and place a receptacle in the middle of the circle such as a bowl, bucket, or (clean) trash container. The container is an imaginal fire pit. Going around the circle, each person imagines throwing something into the pit. Use your arms to symbolically throw or release the item. At the end of the person's throw, the rest of the group says, "A-hoe!" in support and confirmation. Imagine the item dissolving into smoke and rising from the middle up to the sky. In the first round, release something about yourself or your past. Keep the focus on yourself (e.g., fear, anger, worry, etc.). In the second round, release something about the planet (e.g., pollution, disease, child abuse, fear, violence, etc.). In the third round, put in something positive that you want for yourself (e.g., peace, a job, better relationship with my daughter, etc.). In the fourth round, everyone silently puts whatever they want into the fire, releasing something negative or bringing in something positive. Remain silent until everyone is done. Then collectively say a big "a-hoe!" and lift your arms toward the sky.
(This exercise is based on a sacred ritual in Native American culture called a "sweat lodge." Only do this if everyone feels comfortable with the exercise.)

18. *Mindful awareness.* Start with two to three *signal breaths* and then bring the focus on feeling the body supported by the chair, feet on the ground, and spine against the chair. Focus on the breath. If thoughts arise, imagine them passing by like a passing train or put them on a cloud and watch them float across the sky. Without judgment, simply observe the experience of sitting in a chair and breathing. The first day of this section could be "closed-eye awareness" and the next day could be "open-eyed awareness." Some people like to focus on the breath—just noticing the breath going in and out of the nostrils or focusing on the rise and fall of the chest. This simple exercise can be challenging, but with practice can feel centering, grounding, and relaxing. End with two to three *cleansing breaths*.

Mindfulness Script. "First start with two *signal breaths* . . . deep breath in through the nose . . . hold it at the top . . . and then exhale through the mouth. . . . And again, deep breath in through the nose . . . hold it at the top . . . and then exhale through the mouth. . . . Feel yourself sitting in the chair, your feet on the floor and back in an upright position . . . with your arms and hands resting comfortably in your lap. Allow yourself to sink into the chair, relaxing your body, and breathe . . .

"Notice how you feel . . . notice your body . . . notice your breath . . . notice how your body moves with each breath . . . expanding and rising on the inhale . . . and collapsing and falling on the exhale . . . notice the rise. . . and fall of each breath." Wait for a few breaths. "Now bring your awareness of the breath entering and exiting your body . . . through your nose, filling up your lungs and then releasing. Now bring your awareness just to your nostrils. Notice the air going in . . . and out of your nostrils. Without altering or judging . . . just noticing. Being aware of these sensations as you breathe. Staying present with this experience, right here, right now. Just breathing. Maybe you notice a thought pops into your mind or maybe you find that your mind has drifted off somewhere else. . . . Just notice this and gently bring your attention back to this breath. Just noticing these thoughts like passing clouds in the sky—it's there and then it's gone. Bringing your attention to breathing, inhaling and exhaling . . . with awareness. Enjoying this moment of stillness.

"Now bring your awareness to you sitting in the chair, back against the chair, feet on the floor . . . bring your awareness of sitting in this room and others also sitting on chairs. Slowly wiggle your fingers and toes. . . . Let's take two *cleansing breaths*. . . . Deep breath in through the mouth and out with a sigh. Again, and this time really let it all out! . . . in through the mouth and out with a sigh."

CHAPTER 10: EXPLORING BALANCE AND LOVE IMAGERY

19. *Exploring balance.* Everyone finds a partner. Facing each other, they are asked to place both feet facing forward as if they are standing on a line. This is an imaginary log in the water. Participants raise their right hands and then with their right hands reach over to grasp the right wrist of their partner. The object is to maneuver the other person off balance and off the line (into the water!). The first one to move his or her feet off of the line loses. Do a second exercise if there is time, and end with two *signal breaths* and mindful awareness, followed by two *cleansing breaths*.

    Another balance exercise is participants facing back to back with a partner and seeing if they can sit on imaginary chairs with their backs supporting each other. See how deep of a sit the dyad can manage. End with two *signal breaths* and mindful awareness, followed by two *cleansing breaths*.

20. *Love imagery.* Start by taking two *signal breaths* and using aromatherapy. "Feel your feet on the ground and your back against the chair. Feel yourself relax, allowing the chair to completely support you. Now lift your hands and rub your two palms together, building heat between your palms. Place your hands over your heart. Imagine the heat waking up your glowing light inside. Imagine the light, a

beautiful warm golden light, emanating from your heart. Feel this glow spreading through your body, then feel it emanating through your skin around your body, forming a warm glow of light all around you—like a bubble of light.

"Now feel that this light is love. Feel being completely loved. Feel this feeling of warmth and contentment, of peace and well-being from the inside out. Imagine sharing this feeling with someone, thereby intensifying it. Imagine an angel or other loving figure looking at you, smiling, and emanating the same glow. Imagine seeing his or her eyes, filled with love. Feel a slight smile on your face as you see this smile directed at you. Imagine this figure telling you, *'You are loved. You are and always will be loved. Your essence is perfect. You are loved no matter what.'*

"Hold this feeling in your heart and take it with you wherever you go. Take a deep breath in through your nose and let it out through your mouth with a sigh. Again, take a deep breath in through your nose and let it out with a sigh. Feel your feet on the ground and slowly open your eyes." End with two *cleansing breaths*.

CHAPTER 11: STAYING GROUNDED AND ENERGY CLEANSING

21. *Staying grounded.* What are some ways that help you stay grounded, and feel calm and present? Some say walking barefoot on grass or at the beach, eating protein, avoiding sugar and caffeine, wiggling their toes to stay aware of their feet, deep breathing, positive self-talk, and staying hydrated helps. Today's practice is about staying grounded. The first exercise is to become aware of your feet on the ground. First, everyone lifts the toes and then presses down through the feet to feel the floor beneath them. If participants are standing, they should keep a slight bend to the knees. If standing, participants should feel their spines lift toward the sky, chin parallel with the floor, and with arms by their sides press down through the fingertips toward the floor. This stance is lifting and grounding at the same time. Then everyone shakes out their bodies.

    The next exercise is a grounding breath. Everyone sits in a chair. With an inhale, the arms lift up above the head and then with the exhale use the hands to sweep in front of the body (bending the elbows and keeping the hands close to the body), bending forward and ending with the hands sweeping away from the body to the floor. On the inhale the arms lift up and on the exhale the body bends forward with the hands sweeping toward the floor.

    The third exercise is also in the chair. Participants imagine the breath going in through the feet, filling the legs and all the way through the lungs, and then with the exhale imagine the breath leaving all the way through the feet. End with two *signal breaths* and mindful awareness, followed by two *cleansing breaths*.

22. *Energy cleansing.* This class is about moving and clearing energy. Try this ancient yoga exercise: Sit in a chair, rub the hands together, and as if washing the face "splash water on the face." Then take the hands and brush down the back of the head, cross the hands and brush down the upper arms, then bend forward and brush down the legs. Shake the hands out when you are done. Repeat three times. Another exercise is to rub the hands together, creating heat, then place them over the eyes and breathe. A third exercises is to rub the hand together, creating heat, then place them over the heart and breathe. End with two *signal breaths* and mindful awareness, followed by two *cleansing breaths*. (Optional: Add body scan or aromatherapy!)

CHAPTER 12: WHO ARE YOU?

23. *Who are you?* Participants are asked to come up with a positive adjective or description that they believe is an important value, such as loyalty, kindness, or integrity. After participants choose a positive word defining an important aspect of one's self, they introduce themselves to each other (e.g., "Hi, I'm laughter and joy," "Hi, I'm freedom," "Nice to meet you!" "Nice to meet you, too!"). People wander around the room so that everyone has a change to meet each other in the room. *Note:* If you include shaking hands with everyone, some people may want to use a cleansing solution, so pass around a bottle of solution before and after the exercise.End with two *signal breaths* and mindful awareness, followed by two *cleansing breaths*.

24. *Mindful awareness.* The second day of the chapter ends with *mindful awareness.* Start with two to three *signal breaths,* followed by focusing on the breath and then a few minutes of silence. The facilitator can say some positive words, thanking everyone for their participation. This is the last class of new *Warrior Renew* material and next week is review and graduation. This is an opportunity to remind everyone of how well they did and that their healing will continue to unfold even after the class ends. They will continue to synthesize all that they have learned as they embark on their next adventures in life. End with two *cleansing breaths*.

REVIEW WEEK

The first class of this week is an opportunity to review all of the material in the class. One way to do this is to play "Open the Book and Find It!" In this game, the facilitator calls out a question and participants have to find the answer in the book. The first person to find it says, "Found it!" and then recites the answer. The facilitator can use the review questions provided in this book or come up with some of his or her own. Participants can also share what they felt was most helpful for them going through the *Warrior Renew* program. After review class, end with two *signal breaths*, mindful awareness, a few words of gratitude and encouragement from the facilitator, and two to three *cleansing breaths*.

Graduation. For the final day of *Warrior Renew*, the facilitator can administer a written final exam based on the review questions. Another option is to play a game such as Bingo or an elimination competition. If you play Bingo, use this variation: When a number is called that matches a number on players' cards, before they are able to put a marker on the number, they must pick a question and answer it correctly. The first player to reach Bingo wins. For a game such as an elimination competition, everyone sits in a circle. Each person must answer a question to stay in the game. If he or she misses then he or she is out of the game. This can be played individually or in teams. The last one remaining in the game wins. The goal is to have fun and review the material.

After the testing activities, facilitators may sign participants' Certificate of Completion, available at the end of this text. Then everyone sits in a circle and has time to share about their *Warrior Renew* experience and offer gratitude and words of encouragement to each other. Finally, end the day with a few minutes of mindful awareness, closing words from the facilitator, and three good *cleansing breaths*.

Post-graduation party. It is completely up to the participants whether or not to have a post-graduation party.

1. What is the definition of *military sexual trauma*?
2. Why is sexual trauma higher in the military than in civilian society?
3. What are some unique complications of MST?
4. Who are typical perpetrators? And why does this add to the difficulties for sexual trauma survivors?
5. Why do most MST events go unreported?
6. What are *feelings*?
7. What information do the following feelings tell us: anger, fear, sadness, and joy?
8. Name three things you've learned about feelings.
9. How do you know what you are feeling?
10. What is a *neural network*?
11. What is a *signal breath*?
12. What is a *cleansing breath*?
13. Name two things to do if you have a nightmare.
14. What is the *rational* versus *experiential system*?
15. What do we learn from the *lemon exercise*?
16. What is your sleep routine (to prepare you to go to sleep)?
17. Why do we use sachets and other items that smell good after a nightmare?
18. Explain the following normal reactions to stress: fight, flight, freeze, and tend and befriend.
19. How is a PTSD response different from normal reactions to stress?
20. What does COPE stand for?

21. What do you do if you have a panic attack?

22. What is an *experiential hologram*?

23. What's the difference between a *point* and a *vector*?

24. What does the *cupcake exercise* mean?

25. What are the five questions you can use to keep you in the present and out of the holographic trap?

26. What are three common avoidance strategies?

27. What does it mean that anger is an "umbrella" emotion?

28. What is the difference between *rage* and *resentment*?

29. Why do people hold on to resentments?

30. What is *poetic justice*?

31. What is *radical acceptance*?

32. What is healthy self-blame?

33. What is the difference between *behavioral* and *characterological* self-blame?

34. What is the productive value of guilt?

35. Why do people who are grieving experience guilt?

36. Who is a typical perpetrator of sexual trauma?

37. What does it mean to "put blame where blame is due"?

38. How does seeing things from multiple points of view help a victim of sexual trauma?

39. What is needed in order to weaken old associations and patterns and build new associations and patterns (e.g., how do you change your neural networks)?

40. Name three positive attributes about yourself.

41. Name three things you learned in this class.

42. Describe a Stage 1 relationship.

43. Describe a Stage 2 relationship.

44. Describe a Stage 3 relationship.

45. What are the three factors of a balanced relationship (Sternberg's triangles)?

46. What was Harville Hendrix's great discovery?

47. What is a healthy way to develop trust in a relationship?

48. What are three qualities that will enhance a sexual relationship?

49. What should you think about before disclosing your sexual trauma to a romantic partner?

50. Explain how *balance* is an active process.

51. We are prewired to respond to what?

52. Name three emotions associated with grief.

53. What will happen when life isn't the way you expect it or think it should be?

54. What is *delayed grief*?

55. What are Kübler-Ross's five stages of grief?

56. What is an example of traumatic growth?

57. Name three things that you are grateful for.

58. Can the brain of an adult learn new relationship patterns? If so, how?

59. What is the definition of *effective communication*?

60. What are five magic words you can use when someone makes a request of you?

61. What can you say if someone is provoking you into a fight?

62. What is *mindful awareness*?

63. What does *possibilities* mean in this class?

64. Name three things that bring you joy.

65. _____

CERTIFICATE OF COMPLETION

This certifies that

_____

Has successfully completed the *Warrior Renew* program

On this date _____

At this location _____

Facilitator _____

_____

Congratulations!

References

Asch, S. E. (1956). Studies of independence and conformity. A minority of one against a unanimous majority. *Psychological Monographs, 70*(9), 1–70.

Basharpoor, S., Narimani, M., Gamari-give, H., Abolgasemi, A., & Molavi, P. (2011). Effect of cognitive processing therapy and holographic reprocessing on reduction of posttraumatic cognitions in students exposed to trauma. *Iranian Journal of Psychiatry, 6*(4), 138–144.

Boal, A. (1999). *Games for actors and non-actors*. New York, NY: Routledge.

Bowlby, J. (1958). The nature of the child's tie to his mother. *International Journal of Psycho-Analysis, 39*, 1–23.

Bowlby, J. (1988). *A secure base: Parent-child attachment and healthy human development*. New York, NY: Basic Books.

Covey, S. (1989). *The seven habits of highly effective people: Powerful lessons in personal change*. New York, NY: Simon and Schuster.

Doka, K. (Ed.). (1989). *Disenfranchised grief: Recognizing hidden sorrow*. Lexington, MA: Lexington Books.

Epstein, S. (1990). Cognitive-experiential self-theory. In L. Pervin (Ed.), *Handbook of personality theory and research: Theory and research* (pp. 165–192). New York, NY: Guilford Press.

Epstein, S. (1991). Cognitive-experiential self-theory: An integrative theory of personality. In R. Curtis (Ed.), *The relational self: Convergences in psychoanalysis and social psychology* (pp. 111–137). New York, NY: Guilford Press.

Epstein, S. (2014). *Cognitive experiential theory*. London, UK: Oxford University Press.

Foa, E. B., & Rothbaum, B. O. (1998). *Treating the trauma of rape: Cognitive-behavioral therapy for PTSD*. New York, NY: Guilford Press.

Fonagy, P., Steele, M., Steele, H., Leigh, T., Kennedy, R., Mattoon, G., & Target, M. (1995). Attachment, the reflective self, and borderline states: The predictive specificity of the Adult Attachment Interview and pathological emotional development. In S. Goldberg, R. Muir, & J. Kerr (Eds.), *Attachment theory: Social, developmental and clinical perspectives* (pp. 233-278). New York, NY: Analytic Press.

Fontana, A., & Rosenheck, R. (1998). Psychological benefits and liabilities of traumatic exposure in the war zone. *Journal of Traumatic Stress, 11*(3), 485–503.

Freyd, J. J. (1996). *Betrayal trauma: The logic of forgetting childhood abuse.* Cambridge, MA: Harvard University Press.

Gamache, G., Rosenheck, R., & Tessler, R. (2003). Overrepresentation of women veterans among homeless women. *American Journal of Public Health, 93*(7), 1132–1136.

Gendlin, E. T. (2007). *Focusing [Reissue, with new introduction].* New York, NY: Bantam Books.

Goldzweig, C. L., Balekian, T. M., Rolon, C., Yano, E. M., & Shekelle, P. G. (2006). The state of women veterans' health research: Results of a systematic literature review. *Journal of Internal General Medicine, 21*(3), 82–92.

Harlow, H. F. (1962). Development of affection in primates. In E. L. Bliss (Ed.), *Roots of behavior* (pp. 157–166). New York, NY: Harper.

Haskell, S., Gordon, K., Mattocks, K., Duggal, M., Erdos, J., Justice, A., & Brandt, C. (2010). Gender differences in rates of depression, PTSD, pain, obesity, and military sexual trauma among Connecticut war veterans of Iraq and Afghanistan. *Journal of Women's Health (Larchmt), 19*(2), 267–271.

Hendrix, H. (1988). *Getting the love you want: A guide for couples.* New York, NY: Holt.

Hendrix, H. (1992). *Keeping the love you find: A personal guide.* New York, NY: Pocket Books.

Horowitz, M. (1997). *Stress response syndromes: PTSD, grief, and adjustment disorders.* Lanham, MD: Jason Aronson Publishers, Inc.

Kabat-Zinn, J., Wheeler, E., Light, T., Skillings, A., Scharf, M. J., Cropley, T. G., Hosmer, D., & Bernhard, J. D. (1998). Influence of a mindfulness meditation-based stress reduction intervention on rates of skin clearing in patients with moderate to severe psoriasis undergoing phototherapy (UVB) and photochemotherapy (PUVA). *Psychosomatic Medicine, 60*(5), 625–32.

Katz, L. (2001). Holographic reprocessing: A cognitive-experiential psychotherapy for the treatment of trauma. *Psychotherapy: Theory, Research, Practice, and Training, 38*(2), 186–197.

Katz, L. (2005). *Holographic reprocessing: A cognitive-experiential psychotherapy for the treatment of trauma.* New York, NY: Brunner-Routledge.

Katz, L. (2014). *Warrior renew: Healing from military sexual trauma, facilitator's handbook.* Trabuco, CA: Inner Wisdom Press.

Katz, L., Cojucar, G., Beheshti, S., Nakamura, E., & Murray, M. (2012). Military sexual trauma during deployment to Iraq and Afghanistan: Prevalence, readjustment, and gender differences. *Violence and Victims, 27*(4), 487–499.

Katz, L., Douglas, S., Zaleski, K., Williams, J., Huffman, C., & Cojucar, G. (2014). Comparing holographic reprocessing and prolonged exposure for women veterans with sexual trauma: A pilot randomized trial. *Journal of Contemporary Psychotherapy, 44*, 9–19. doi:10.1007/s1079-013-9248-6

Katz, A., & Katz, L. (in press). *Norma and Newman.* Trabuco Canyon, CA: Inner Wisdom Press.

Katz, L., Snetter, M., Hagler, A., Hewitt, P., & Cojucar, G. (2008). Holographic reprocessing: Empirical evidence to reduce posttraumatic cognitions in women veterans with PTSD from sexual trauma and abuse. *Psychotherapy: Theory, Research, Practice, and Training, 45*(2), 186–198.

Kimmerling, R., Street, A., Pavao, J., Smith, M., Cronkite, C., Holmes, T., & Frayne, S. (2010). Military-related sexual trauma among veterans health administration patients returning from Afghanistan and Iraq. *American Journal of Public Health, 100*(8), 1409–1412.

Kübler-Ross, E. (1997). *On death and dying.* New York, NY: Scribner.

Linehan, M. (1993). *Skills training manual for treating borderline personality disorder.* New York, NY: Guilford Press.

Maltz, W. (2012). *The sexual healing journey: A guide for survivors of sexual abuse* (3rd ed.). New York, NY: Harper Collins.

McIsaac, H. K., & Eich, E. (2002). Vantage point in episodic memory. *Psychonomic Bulletin Review, 9*, 146–150.

McIsaac, H. K., & Eich, E. (2004). Vantage point in traumatic memory. *Psychological Science, 15*(4), 248–253.

Myss, C. (1997). *Anatomy of the spirit.* New York, NY: Three Rivers Press.

Peitsch, P. (1981). *Shufflebrain.* Boston, MA: Houghton Mifflin.

Pennebaker, J. (1997). Writing about emotional experiences as a therapeutic process. *Psychological Science, 8*(3), 162–166.

Pribram, K. (1991). *Brain and perception: Holonomy and structure in figural processing.* Hillsdale, NJ: Lawrense Erlbaum Associates.

Resnick, H. S., Kilpatrick, D. G., Dansky, B. S., Saunders, B. E., & Best, C. L. (1993). Prevalence of civilian trauma and posttraumatic stress disorder in a representative national sample of women. *Journal of Consulting and Clinical Psychology, 61*(6), 984–991.

Sternberg, Robert J. (2004). A triangular theory of love. In H. T. Reis & C. E. Rusbult (Eds.), *Close relationships* (pp. 258–276). New York, NY: Psychology Press.

Suris, A., & Lind, L. (2008). Military sexual trauma: A review of prevalence and associated health consequences in veterans. *Trauma Violence Abuse, 9*(4), 250–269.

Taylor, S., Klein, L., Lewis, B., Gruenewald, T., Gurung, R., & Updegraff, J. (2000). Behavioral responses to stress in females: Tend and befriend not fight or flight, *Psychological Review, 107*(3), 411–429.

Wallin, D. J. (2007). *Attachment in psychotherapy.* New York, NY: Guilford Press.

Washington, D. L., Yano, E. M., McGuire, J., Hines, V., Lee, M., & Gelberg, L. (2010). Risk factors for homelessness among women veterans. *Journal of Health Care for the Poor and Underserved, 21*(1), 81–91.

Yehuda, R., Bierer, L. M., Schmeidler, J., Aferiat, D. H., Breslau, I., Dolan, S. (2000). Low cortisol and risk for PTSD in adult offspring of holocaust survivors, *American Journal of Psychiatry*, *157*(8), 1252–1259.

Parts of this book have been adapted from the following Inner Wisdom Press workbooks:

Katz, L. (2006a). *50 ways to deal with feelings: Skills to understand, identify, tolerate, manage, and shift through feelings.* Trabuco Canyon, CA: Inner Wisdom Press.

Katz, L. (2006b). *Journey to your heart: Stories and lessons to open your heart to healthier and happier relationships.* Trabuco Canyon, CA: Inner Wisdom Press.

Katz, L., & Hammerslough, J. (2012). *Self-care for women: For a healthy and balanced life.* Trabuco Canyon, CA: Inner Wisdom Press.

Index

CPSIA information can be obtained
at www.ICGtesting.com
Printed in the USA
BVOW04s1148180717
489516BV00016B/69/P

9 780826 122315